Please remember that this is a library book,
and that it belongs only temporarily to each
person who uses it. Be considerate. Do
not write in this, or any, library book.

APPLICATIONS OF INFORMATION THEORY
TO PSYCHOLOGY

FRED ATTNEAVE

University of Oregon

Applications
of Information Theory
to Psychology:

A SUMMARY OF BASIC CONCEPTS,

METHODS, AND RESULTS

HOLT, RINEHART AND WINSTON

New York — Chicago — San Francisco — Toronto — London

5   6   7   8   9

2046258

Printed in the United States of America

FOREWORD

THE IDEA that information is something measurable in precise terms was not widely appreciated until 1948, when Norbert Wiener's book *Cybernetics* appeared and Claude E. Shannon published a pair of articles titled "The Mathematical Theory of Communication" in the *Bell System Technical Journal*. Psychologists reading Wiener for the first time were perhaps more impressed by his discussion of feedback, and machines which display purposive behavior, than by the suggestions for quantifying information which his book contained. The quick spread of Shannon's ideas beyond the field of engineering may be attributed largely to a skillful and imaginative introductory article by Warren Weaver which appeared in the July 1949 issue of *Scientific American* and was later published together with Shannon's articles in book form [79]. George A. Miller and Frederick C. Frick published, also in 1949, an article [57] which first clearly demonstrated the relevance of information theory to psychology, with a method for quantifying organization or patterning in sequences of events which will be described in Chapter 2.

Thus presented with a shiny new tool kit and a somewhat esoteric new vocabulary to go with it, more than a few psychologists reacted with an excess of enthusiasm. During the early fifties some of the attempts to apply informational techniques to psychological problems were successful and illuminating, some were pointless, and some were downright bizarre. At present two generalizations may be stated with considerable confidence: (1) Information theory is not going to provide a ready-made solution to all psychological problems; (2) Employed with intelligence, flexibility, and critical insight, information theory can have great value both in the formulation of certain psychological problems and in the analysis of certain psychological data.

This volume represents a first attempt to set forth a comprehensive summary of informational methods useful in psychological research as they have been developed up to the present time. The more important of them will be described in enough detail to make them available to the reader as practical research tools. At the same time, I shall endeavor to convey a basic appreciation of what such methods involve and accomplish, so that the reader may be able to employ them appropriately (or not at all) and to interpret them intelligently. Since disembodied methodology is seldom inspiring, the uses to which information theory has so far been put in psychology, and the findings which have resulted, will be discussed at some length. Of considerable interest are those areas in which the informational concepts have contributed to a reformulation of old problems in terms which suggest new and profitable lines of investigation.

It should perhaps be stated explicitly that this book is not written as a vehicle for original contributions of my own; anyone who has followed closely the psychological applications of information theory will find little here that is new to him. My aim is rather to impart a basic knowledge of the subject to the reader whose prior acquantance with it is minimal.

F. A.

Eugene, Oregon
March, 1959

CONTENTS

CHAPTER 1

"Information": From Intuitive to Quantitative Concepts

T HE TECHNICAL MEANING of "information"is not radically different from the everyday meaning; it is merely more precise. Information is something which we gain by reading, or listening, or by directly observing the world about us. A statement or an observation is informative if it tells us something we did not already know. If I hear someone say "Eskimos live in the far North, where it is cold," my modest store of information about Eskimos is not increased. The statement may, however, give me some information about the person who makes it, or about the person to whom it is addressed.

In any case, we can gain information only about matters in which we are to some degree ignorant, or uncertain: indeed, information may be defined as that which removes or reduces uncertainty. The important implication of this definition is that once we are able to measure uncertainty, we can also measure information in similar terms. Let us, then, consider how an amount or degree of uncertainty might be specified. If I wish to find a book which I have been reading, and I am unable to specify the particular place where I left it, I say that I am uncertain of its location. If I know that it is in one of two places, I can still find it without much trouble; if it might be in any of a dozen places, my uncertainty is greater; and if it is equally likely to be in any one of a hundred places, my uncertainty is very great indeed. In general, it seems reasonable to maintain that the uncertainty of a question increases with the number of alternative answers it might have (provided the different answers are equally probable). Thus the result of throwing a die is more uncertain than that of tossing a coin, since a die may fall in six ways and a coin in only two; more uncertain than either is the draw of a card from a deck, in which case there are 52 alternative outcomes. We could, if we wished, define uncertainty as *equal to* the number of alternatives, but we shall presently see that the logarithm of this number provides a unit which is more satisfying, both intuitively and mathematically.

The old parlor game of "Twenty Questions," recently revived on radio and television and in psychological laboratories [10], is a good illustration of gradual uncertainty-reduction. One of the players announces, "I am thinking of something Animal" (or "Vegetable," or "Mineral," as the case may be), and the others proceed to ask him questions to which he can answer "Yes" or "No." Their goal is to discover what he has in mind by asking not more than twenty such questions. Now, consider a simplified version of this game in which the thing being thought of is a particular square on a checkerboard, and the task of the questioner is merely to discover *which* of the 64 possible squares it is. It is easy to show that exactly six questions, properly asked, are always necessary and sufficient to locate the square. These questions might take the following form:

1. Is it one of the 32 on the left half of the board? (Yes)
2. Is it one of the 16 in the upper half of the 32 remaining? (No)
3. Is it one of the 8 in the left half of the 16 remaining? (No)
4. Is it one of the 4 in the upper half of the 8 remaining? (No)
5. Is is one of the 2 in the left half of the 4 remaining? (Yes)
6. Is it the upper one of the 2 remaining? (Yes)

The parenthetical answers refer to Figure 1, which shows how the area of uncertainty is progressively reduced until the square is located. The questions could be arranged in other ways equally efficient (for example, the first three could be

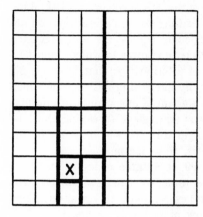

FIG. 1. Showing how uncertainty about the location of a square on a checkerboard is reduced, in terms of the "Twenty Questions" model.

left-right questions, restricting the square to a single column, and the next three up-down questions, restricting it to a row), but it is essential that every question reduce the alternatives which remain by half, rather than by any other fraction; otherwise more than six questions will sometimes be required.

If the questions are always asked in the same way, any sequence of six *Yes*'s and *No*'s will yield a unique cell on the checkerboard. Letting 1 mean *Yes* and 0 mean *No*, 100011 will represent the cell illustrated in Figure 1, 010000 the cell in column 8, row 4, and so forth. In other words, six binary digits are needed to specify or represent one alternative out of 64. The binary number system has the same general properties as the decimal system, with which we are more familiar, but it uses only two different symbols (zero and one) instead of ten. In the decimal system, one digit is necessary to specify one alternative out of 10^1 or 10, two to specify one alternative out of 10^2 or 100, three to specify one alternative out of 10^3 or 1000, and so on. Likewise, in binary numbers, a single digit specifies a choice from 2 alternatives, two digits specify one of 2^2 or 4 alternatives, and six digits specify one of 2^6 or 64 alternatives, the number on our checkerboard.

The binary digit, or *bit*, as it is called in abbreviated form, is the unit most often used in the measurement of information and uncertainty. Thus we say that the uncertainty involved in the question "Which square on the checkerboard am I thinking about?" amounts to six bits, or that six bits of information are required to designate a particular square. It was suggested above that the number of bits is the power to which 2 must be raised to equal the number of alternatives: that is, $m = 2^H$, where m is the number of equally likely alternatives from which a choice is made, and H is the amount of uncertainty or information, expressed in bits. This is equivalent to saying that the number of bits equals the logarithm, to the base 2†, of the number of alternatives: that is, $H = \log m$.

In Appendix II, on page 99, is a table of $\log n$ for values of n up to 1000. From this table we can read directly the amount of uncertainty (in bits) associated with various numbers of alternatives. For the throw of a die, $H = \log 6 = 2.58$; for the draw of a card, $H = \log 52 = 5.70$. The reader may easily verify, in terms of the "Twenty Questions" model, that either two or three questions are needed for the identification of a face of the die, and that either five or six will reveal which of the 52 cards was chosen. It should be emphasized, however, that one bit is the *maximum* amount of information contained in a Yes-or-No answer, and that this maximum is achieved only when the question is asked in such a way as to split the possibilities exactly in half, so that "Yes" and "No" are equally likely as answers. Even in very simple cases it is impossible to ask the question in this way if the remaining alternatives are not evenly divisible by 2, and in the case of the regular game it is generally impossible because the probabilities can only be estimated in the crudest way; nevertheless it is characteristic of good playing to approach this goal as nearly as the

---

† Whenever the terms "logarithm" or "log" are subsequently used in this book without subscript or other qualification, it should be understood that the base 2 is implied. If any other base is intended, it will be explicitly indicated: for example, "$\log_{10}$" or "$\log_e$."

circumstances allow. Under ideal conditions, the full set of 20 questions could identify one concept out of a class of 2^{20}, or 1,048,576. Since the concept is identified fairly often under conditions which are by no means ideal, it seems likely that most people have somewhat fewer than a million concepts in each of the classes "Animal," "Vegetable," and "Mineral," even when the outlandish and improbable are included.

A practically infallible procedure for winning the game (and losing friends) is to choose a concept involving some *number* greater than 20^{20}—for example, "962,428,812 ducks." An interesting problem arises here: since the class of all numbers is infinite, it would appear that an infinite amount of information must be involved in the specification of any particular number. The reason why this is not true is that the number of *specifiable* numbers is *not* infinite. The class of numbers which can be spoken or written within any finite interval, such as a lifetime, has only a finite number of members. Numbers of very great magnitude may be designated by the use of exponents, but these are special, "round," numbers in between which lie many numbers too long for anyone ever to write out. Another case which seems to involve infinite information is that of a point on a line. To specify one of the infinite points making up a geometrical line, an infinite amount of information would indeed be required. In practice, however, the position of a point can never be determined without some degree of error— for example, the precision of a yardstick is ultimately limited by its molecular grain. Error of measurement has the effect of dividing any continuum into a limited number of alternative categories which can be accurately discriminated from one another. In general, whenever it appears that we are able to deal with infinite quantities of information, we find that we have overlooked some limiting factor which reduces the number of practical alternatives in the situation to a finite level.

Let us next consider how we shall measure information when the alternatives from which a choice is made are *not* equally likely. To recapitulate a little: with m equiprobable alternatives, we arrived at the simple equation

$$H = \log m \qquad (1)$$

Since the m alternatives are equally likely, the probability p of any one is equal to $\dfrac{1}{m}$, and conversely m is equal to $\dfrac{1}{p}$; hence

$$H = \log \frac{1}{p} \tag{2}$$

Now, this measure may be generalized to cases in which the various alternatives have unequal probabilities. Letting h_i stand for the information involved in the occurrence of a particular alternative i (H will be used only when all the alternatives are represented in a single measure), we may write the analogous expression

$$h_i = \log \frac{1}{p_i} \tag{3}$$

Suppose that a bent coin lands "heads" nine-tenths of the time, and "tails" the other tenth; that is, that p (heads) = .90 and p (tails) = .10. According to equation (3), the information associated with a fall of "heads" will be

$$h \text{ (heads)} = \log \frac{1}{.90} = \log 1.11 = .15 \text{ bits}$$

and that associated with "tails" will be

$$h \text{ (tails)} = \log \frac{1}{.10} = \log 10 = 3.32 \text{ bits}$$

The disparity between these figures is plausible in terms of our intuitive notions of information. Prior to any particular throw of the biased coin, we may be fairly sure that it will fall "heads." It it does, the actual event gives us little information, merely confirming our a priori expectation. If it falls "tails," however, we are informed of something which we did not anticipate— the event is "news." (The old man-bites-dog principle of journalism may be considered to have the aim of giving the reader as much information for his money as possible.)

The informational value of a particular event, $h = \log \dfrac{1}{p}$, is sometimes called the *surprisal* of the event [75]. This term is useful because it refers unequivocally to a particular event (or kind of event), not to a whole range of alternatives as is usually the case with *information*, and necessarily the case with *uncertainty*. The reader should be warned, however, that events with equal surprisal values may not be equally surprising to an observer. If a number between 1 and 10 is randomly chosen, whatever number is actually drawn—say, 8—has the same surprisal $\left(\log \frac{1}{.10} = \log 10 = 3.32 \right)$ as a throw of "tails" with the biased coin. It is less surprising, however, because the number drawn is no more improbable than any other number would have been. Whereas surprisal (as defined above) is a simple function of the probability of an event, surprise (in a psychological sense) seems to depend on the probability of the event relative to the probabilities of other alternatives.

Returning to our biased coin: if we take the mean of all the h's which would be obtained over a long series of throws, we arrive at a value for H, the uncertainty or average information associated with a throw. Whenever a "heads" occurs, .15 will be contributed to the average; whenever a "tails" occurs, 3.32 will be contributed. We know, however, that "heads" will be thrown nine times as often as "tails;" therefore the average of these two values should be a weighted one, with "heads" contributing nine-tenths of the weight, and "tails" only one tenth. In other words, a fair average of the two h-values is obtained *by weighting each value with its probability*. Thus

$$H = .90 \times .15 + .10 \times 3.32 = .47 \text{ bits}$$

The reader will not be surprised to find that less uncertainty is associated with a throw of this biased coin than with a throw of a straight coin, for which H is of course equal to one bit.

The procedure just followed in calculating H should now be formalized a little, and put in terms which apply to any number of alternatives. For m alternatives, each with its own p and h, the formula used above for a weighted average may be written as follows:

$$H = p_1 h_1 + p_2 h_2 \cdots + p_i h_i \cdots + p_m h_m \qquad (4)$$

or, $\qquad H = \sum^{i} p_i h_i \qquad (4a)$

That is, the uncertainty or average information associated with an event is equal to the sum of the information values, or surprisals, of all the individual alternatives (i stands for any alternative) with each multiplied by its probability as a weighting factor.

Since h is equal to $\log \dfrac{1}{p}$, we may state the formula entirely in terms of p, if we wish:

$$H = \sum^{i} p_i \log \frac{1}{p_i} \tag{5}$$

This is often called the Shannon-Wiener measure of information. It is sometimes written

$$H = -\sum^{i} p_i \log p_i \tag{5a}$$

since one of the rules for manipulating logarithms is that $\log \dfrac{1}{x} = -\log x$.

It is important that the reader clearly understand the rationale of formula (5); before proceeding, he should convince himself that it actually represents a properly weighted average (not a total, as the summation sign suggests) of the information involved in individual alternative events.† It should further be noted that in any case of equiprobable alternatives—that is, when all values of p_i are equal—formula (5) simplifies to formula (2), thus:

$$H = \Sigma p \log \frac{1}{p} = (\Sigma p) \log \frac{1}{p} = \log \frac{1}{p}$$

The terms "uncertainty" and "average information" (or simply "information," with the "average" understood) are used almost interchangeably to refer to that property of a set of events which is symbolized by H. "Uncertainty" suggests future events, and "information" past events, but the statistical property in question is measured in the same way no matter

---

† The general procedure for taking a weighted average is to multiply each number by its weighting factor, summate, and then divide by the sum of the weighting factors. When probabilities are used as weights, however, no explicit dividing operation is necessary, because the sum of the p's is always 1.

when the events occur. A third, somewhat older name for this property is "entropy." The term "entropy," defined as in formula (5), has been used in statistical mechanics since the last century to refer to the randomness, or unpredictability, of a physical system such as a chamber of gas molecules. For any given number of alternatives, m, the greatest possible value of H is $\log m$ or $\log \frac{1}{p}$, which occurs (as we have seen) only when the alternatives are equiprobable. It is often convenient to describe a particular value of H as a proportion of this maximum:

$$R = \frac{H}{H_{max}} = \frac{H}{\log m} \qquad (6)$$

R is called the *relative entropy* of a set of events. The complementary quantity, $C = 1 - R$, is known as *redundancy*. For our biased coin,

$$R = \frac{H}{H_{max}} = \frac{.47}{1} = .47$$

The *redundancy* of a series of throws, $1 - R$, is equal to .53, or 53 percent. What this statement means will become clearer in the discussion to follow.

It was not difficult to see, in the case of the checkerboard and other situations which involve equiprobable alternatives, that H represents the *minimum number of binary digits into which an event may be encoded*. We showed, for example, how any one of the 64 squares on the checkerboard could be symbolized by a series of six zero's and one's. It is not so obvious, but is nevertheless true, that this interpretation of H remains valid for situations involving alternatives of unequal probability (with the qualification that H is always an average in such situations). The value of $H = .47$ for the biased coin means literally that an average of only 47 binary digits are necessary to describe perfectly a series of 100 throws, provided this information is encoded in the most efficient way. If no code were employed, and the symbols 0 and 1 were used directly to stand for "heads" and "tails," respectively, 100 throws would require a series of 100 binary digits. Such a series would be redundant, however, since by means of proper encoding its length could be reduced by about 53 percent.

At this point we encounter one of the most frustrating peculiarities of information theory. Although we can determine, by calculating H, how many binary digits per event are required with optimal encoding, the actual devising of this optimal code is an altogether different and more difficult problem, for which no general solution has ever been worked out. Faced with an actual need for an efficient code, one may find it practical to compromise on a solution somewhat less than perfect.

Working out a near-optimal code for the biased coin will demonstrate, on a concrete level, some of the principles and problems involved in efficient coding. Let us start by breaking down the sequence of throws into groups of seven. A group *may* contain any number of "tails" from zero to seven, but the groups which occur most frequently will contain few or none. (Remember that the probability of "tails" on each throw is only 1 in 10.) The probabilities for various numbers of "tails," calculated by Bernoulli's Theorem†, are as follows:

Number of tails:	Probability that a group of 7 throws will contain this number of tails:
0	.478
1	.372
2	.124
3	.023
4	.0026
5	.00017
6	.0000063
7	.0000001

---

† According to Bernoulli's Theorem, if one of the possible outcomes of an event has the probability p, then the probability that r out of n such events will have this outcome is $\dfrac{n!}{r!(n-r)!} (p)^r (1-p)^{n-r}$. In the present case, $p = .1$, $n = 7$, and r varies from 0 to 7. The fractional portion of the expression gives the number of ways in which r tails may occur; the remaining portion constitutes the probability for each of these ways (or permutations). The reader may consult almost any introductory treatment of the theory of probability for an explanation of this theorem.

Now, what we wish to do is to use short code symbols to stand for frequently occurring groups, and longer symbols to stand for less frequently occurring groups. Since almost half the groups will contain no tails at all, let us use the symbol 0 to mean that the group being described contains *no* tails, and the symbol 1 to mean that it contains *some*. The symbol 0 will completely describe tailless groups, but an initial 1 must be followed by additional symbols indicating the *number* and *location* of tails.

Consider first the encoding of *location*. There are eight possible three-bit symbols: 000, 001, 011, 100, 101, 110, and 111; the first seven of these may be used to designate the seven possible locations in a group. The eighth symbol, "111," will be needed only if the group contains more than one tail, in which case it will appear as many times as there are tails *in excess of one*, followed by an appropriate number of location symbols. A minute economy may be achieved by letting the location symbols refer either to tails or to heads, whichever are fewer in number.

The code may be summarized as follows:

(1) If a group of 7 throws contains no tails, it is symbolized with a 0; if it contains one or more tails, it is symbolized with a 1 followed by

(2) the symbol "111" repeated as many times as there are tails in excess of one (that is, 111 = 2 tails, 111111 = 3 tails, and so forth) followed by

(3) one or more location symbols (3-bit symbols other than "111") indicating the serial positions of either the tails or the heads, whichever are fewer.

Counting up the number of binary digits required to represent groups containing various numbers of tails, we find the following:

Number of tails in group	Number of binary digits used to encode group
0	1
1	4
2	10
3	16
4	19
5	19
6	19
7	19

An average value may be obtained by the weighting method discussed earlier: multiplying each of the values in this table by the corresponding probabilities given in the previous table and summating, we find that an average of 3.62 binary digits are used to encode a group of 7 throws. This corresponds to an average of .52 bits per throw, which is not grossly in excess of the .47 attainable with a perfect code.

The reader who enjoys puzzles will not find it difficult to improve upon this code. Some improvement may be achieved without increasing the number of throws per group beyond 7 (for example, a few additional complications would enable us to encode a 2-tail group with 9 instead of 10 digits), but in general, greater efficiency requires longer groupings. Indeed, a *perfect* code may be possible only with an *infinitely* long group of events. In any case, grouping involves the "storage" of events over some period of time before they can be encoded; therefore, the efficient encoding of a sequence, in a communications system, may be achieved only at the expense of some time delay.

This much has been said about efficient encoding not because we shall have any subsequent need to devise codes, but rather with the aim of tying down the concept of redundancy, and the meaning of specific values of H, to fairly concrete operations. In the following chapter we shall see something of the usefulness of these concepts to the psychologist.

The Uncertainty and Redundancy of Happenings in a Sequence

A FUNDAMENTAL IDEA in information theory is that of the *stochastic process*. A stochastic process is any system which gives rise to a sequence of symbols to which probability laws apply. It may be extremely simple, like the tossed coin we have been considering, or extremely complex, as in the case of a sequence of musical notes written by a composer, or a sequence of letters and words making up English text. A stochastic process is said to be *ergodic* if the probability laws which characterize it remain constant for all parts of the sequence. Ergodicity, or at least an approximation thereto, is usually a necessary condition for the application of information measures to a sequence: the reader can readily appreciate the difficulty which would be created if, for example, the bias on the coin which we have discussed were changed in an erratic manner between throws.

A stochastic process is characterized by some degree of redundancy between 0 percent and 100 percent. At the zero-redundancy extreme, all the symbols generated have equal probability of occurrence, and nothing that we may know about the history of the sequence makes the next symbol any more predictable. At the opposite extreme, at 100 percent redundancy, symbols are generated in an altogether lawful and regular sequence, such that one can predict with complete certainty what the next symbol will be. Although the most interesting sequences fall somewhere between these two extremes, it is instructive to consider the variety of ways in which a sequence may be completely redundant. The simplest kind of complete redundancy occurs when one symbol has a probability of one, and others have zero probability, so that the the sequence is of the form AAAAAA · · · . This state of affairs was approached in the case of the biased coin. Redundancy which thus depends upon unequal probabilities of individual symbols is said to be of the *first order*. A simple alternation of the form ABABABAB · · · is also completely redundant, even though A's and B's occur with equal frequency. Such a sequence, in which prediction of a given symbol is possible if the immediately preceding symbol is known, is said to have *second-order* redundancy. A double alternation of the form AABBAABBAABB · · · has *third-order* redundancy, since prediction of a given symbol depends upon a knowledge of the two preceding ones.

Here is another way of looking at the matter. A sequence has Nth-order redundancy whenever some of the possible patterns of N successive symbols are more probable than others. In a simple alternation, for example (illustrating 100 percent redundancy of the second order), the pairs AB and BA occur with equal probability ($p = .50$), but the pairs AA and BB never occur ($p = 0$). Therefore a pair from the sequence, considered in isolation, contains only one bit of information instead of two; in other words, no *new* information is added by the second member of the pair. Likewise in the case of a double alternation (third-order redundancy), only four of the eight possible patterns of three successive symbols ever occur; therefore an isolated triplet contains only two (log 4) instead of three (log 8) bits—that is, the third symbol adds no new information. It may appear at present that we are unnecessarily complicating the obvious, but this way of conceptualizing redundancy will prove important when we come to consider the statistical analysis of binary sequences.

The reader should not rashly conclude, from the above illustrations, that a binary sequence with second-order redundancy always tends toward simple alternation, nor that third-order redundancy necessarily implies a tendency toward double alternation. For example, a sequence of the form AAAAAABBBBBBBBBBAAAAA $\cdots$, in which the same symbol tends to be repeated many times before an alternation occurs (that is, in which the pairs AA and BB are more probable than the pairs AB and BA), also displays second-order redundancy. To the degree that a sequence is redundant, it is in some manner regular, or lawful. Any order of redundancy above the first implies that the events are more or less patterned; that *sequential dependencies* exist among them. But neither the degree nor the order of the redundancy tells us specifically what *kind* of lawfulness, or patterning, is involved. In order to describe a stochastic process completely, it is necessary to specify the probability of every possible sequence of N symbols or alternative events, N being the greatest range of sequential dependencies involved in the process. This is equivalent to specifying (1) the probability of every possible sequence of $N - 1$ events, and (2) for every such sequence, the probabilities of its being followed by the various alternative events (for example, the probability that, if AABAB has just occurred, the next symbol will be A. This is known as a *transitional probability*; what we also need to specify is the probability with which AABAB will itself occur.).

The English language may be considered a stochastic process; as such, it has recently been subjected to a great deal of study by psychologists and communications engineers. Shannon has found, by the use of methods which will be discussed later, that printed English is about 75 percent redundant. To describe English completely as a stochastic process by specifying the probabilities mentioned in the preceding paragraph is quite unfeasible because of the very high orders of redundancy, or sequential dependency, which are involved. Certain low-order probability laws of the language are well known, however:

years ago cryptographers compiled tables of relative frequency for individual letters, digrams (letter pairs), and trigrams.

Shannon has demonstrated a fascinating series of stochastic processes generating "artificial languages" with the same low-order probability laws as the English language. As the order of the probability laws taken from English is increased, the output of the process becomes strikingly more similar to English. The following illustrations are from Shannon [79, pp. 13–14]:

(1) *Zero-order approximation to English.* A completely random selection of characters from an "alphabet" composed of the 26 letters and a space yields this sort of sequence:

XFOML RXKHRJFFJUJ ZLPWCFWKCYJ
FFJEYVKCOQSGHYD ZPAAMKBZAACIBZLJQD.

(2) *First-order approximation.* A table of random numbers was used in conjunction with a table of individual letter-frequencies to choose successive letters independently, but with each letter having the same probability it has in English:

OCRO HLI RGWR NMIELWIS EU LL
NBNESENYA TH EEI ALHENHTTPA OOBTTVA
NAH BRL.

(3) *Second-order approximation.* In this process, the digram structure is the same as that of English; that is, the probability with which each letter follows the one that has just occurred is the same as in English. Shannon constructed this sequence, and those of higher order, by an ingenious short-cut technique. He began by selecting at random a letter from a book, and recording it. Opening the book at another page, he read until this letter occurred, and recorded the succeeding one. He then searched for the second letter on another page, and recorded the one succeeding it, and so on. The result was as follows:

ON IE ANTSOUTINYS ARE T INCTORE ST BE S
DEAMY ACHIN D ILONASIVE TUCOOWE AT
TEASONARE FUSO TIZIN ANDY TOBE SEACE
CTISBE.

(4) *Third-order approximation.* Here the trigram structure is that of English. The method of construction was the same as that described above, except that each *pair* of letters just recorded was found on a new page, and the succeeding letter recorded:

IN NO IST LAT WHEY CRATICT FROURE BIRS GROCID PONDENOME OF DEMONSTURES OF THE REPTAGIN IS REGOACTIONA OF CRE.

(5) *First-order word approximation.* "Rather than continue with tetragram, $\cdots$, N-gram structure," explains Shannon, "it is easier and better to jump at this point to word units. Here words are chosen independently but with their appropriate frequencies":

REPRESENTING AND SPEEDILY IS AN GOOD APT OR COME CAN DIFFERENT NATURAL HERE HE THE A IN CAME THE TO OF TO EXPERT GRAY COME TO FURNISHES THE LINE MESSAGE HAD BE THESE.

(6) *Second-order word approximation.* This sample was constructed by the same technique as (3) above, except that the units are words instead of letters:

THE HEAD AND IN FRONTAL ATTACK ON AN ENGLISH WRITER THAT THE CHARACTER OF THIS POINT IS THEREFORE ANOTHER METHOD FOR THE LETTERS THAT THE TIME OF WHO EVER TOLD THE PROBLEM FOR AN UNEXPECTED.

The progression of these samples toward English is striking. Under (4) we find groups of letters which obviously *could* be words ("grocid pondenome" is almost worthy of Lewis Carroll), and in (6) the discourse approaches a sort of schizoid plausibility. Shannon remarks upon the interesting fact that reasonable sequences are found over about twice the range of the probability relationships used in their construction: for example, most of the four-word sequences in (6) could occur in meaningful English sentences.

It is a well-established principle of verbal learning that "meaningful" material is remembered more easily than "nonsense" material. It occurred to Miller and Selfridge [60] that this difference might be attributable not to meaningfulness per se, but rather to sequential associations of the sort demonstrated by Shannon—in other words, to the greater redundancy, or lower informational content, of meaningful material. They constructed sequences of *words* varying in approximation to English from zero order to seventh order. Since Shannon's method of searching for a sequence in a new context is too laborious to be used to obtain approximations of higher orders, Miller and Selfridge devised a new technique. To construct an Nth-order approximation, they showed a sequence of $N - 1$ words to a person who was instructed to use this sequence in a sentence. "Then the word he used directly after the sequence would be added, the first word of the sequence would be dropped, and the new (but overlapping) sequence would be presented to the next person," and so on to as many additional people as necessary to obtain a sample of the desired length. The samples so constructed, as well as passages of English text, were then read to subjects who attempted, immediately after the reading of each sample, to reproduce what they had heard. The hypothesis of Miller and Selfridge was neatly confirmed by their results: as order of approximation to English increased from 0 to 5, so did percent of words correctly recalled. However, fifth-order approximations (sample: "road in the country was insane especially in dreary rooms where they have some books to buy for studying Greek") were recalled very nearly as well as English text. The authors conclude that "The significant distinction is not to be drawn between meaning and nonsense but between materials that utilize previous learning and permit positive transfer and materials that do not. If the nonsense preserves the short-range associations of the English language that are so familiar to us, the nonsense is easy to learn."

This conclusion may go somewhat too far. Marks and Jack [47] did a subsequent study using similar materials, but scoring subjects on memory span (whereas Miller and Selfridge had scored number of words correctly recalled, regardless of order). Although the average span of words correctly recalled increased steadily with order of approximation to English, the greatest increase (from 10 to 15 words) occurred between the fifth-order approximation and English text. Marks and Jack conclude that meaning does have a facilitating effect on immediate memory, over and above the reduction in information which it entails.

A highly capable engineer who contributes articles to *Astounding Science Fiction* under the name "J. J. Coupling" independently and simultaneously devised the technique used by Miller and Selfridge to construct higher-order approximations to English [21]. Like Miller and Selfridge, Coupling was uncertain of the appropriateness of calling such approximations "meaningful." Since it appeared to him that a condition of meaningfulness might be the presence of some single integrative idea, or theme, he employed the further device of supplying such a theme (for example, *salaries, murder story*, or *women*) to all the individuals contributing to the construction of a sequence. This technique is one that might well be used in psychological investigation. In any case, it is capable of yielding some highly entertaining sequences, like the following fourth-order approximation on the theme *murder story*: "When I killed her I stabbed Paul between his powerful jaws clamped tightly together. Screaming loudly despite fatal consequences in the struggle for life began ebbing as he coughed hollowly spitting blood from his ears."

Let us turn from this diverting byway to the consideration of a new and important question. Given a sequence of symbols (or symbolizable events) which is to some unknown degree redundant, or patterned, or lawful, containing sequential dependencies of the kind we have been discussing, how does one go about calculating the degree of redundancy or patterning? Or, to put the question in its complementary form: how does one calculate the average *net* quantity of information per symbol in a sequence?

In order to perform such a calculation, we must decide how high an order of redundancy we wish to take into account. The higher the order to which the analysis is extended, the greater is the labor of computation and the lower the reliability of the resulting estimate; on the other hand, if the sequence contains dependencies of an order higher than that taken into account by the analysis, the informational content will be overestimated. We saw earlier that information, in bits-per-symbol, is equal to the log of the number of alternative symbols when all symbols are independent and equiprobable. Let us call this a zero-order estimate of H:

$$H_0 = \Sigma p \log \frac{1}{p} = m\left(\frac{1}{m} \log m\right) = \log m$$

since it assumes that the highest order of redundancy involved is zero. Likewise, a first-order estimate of H†

$$\hat{H}_1 = \Sigma \hat{p}_i \log \frac{1}{\hat{p}_i}$$

assumes the absence of any redundancy of order higher than the first (that is, symbols independent but varying in probability, as was the case with the biased coin discussed earlier).

The calculation of a second-order estimate, $\hat{H}_2$, involves the use of a trick which applies as well to higher-order estimates, and which the reader should take pains to understand thoroughly. First the average information in a digram, or pair of consecutive symbols, is calculated just as if each pair were a separate symbol:

$$\hat{H} \text{ (digram)} = \Sigma \hat{p} \text{ (digram)} \log \frac{1}{\hat{p} \text{ (digram)}}$$

where the $\hat{p}$ (digram)'s are the proportions of all (overlapping) pairs falling into the various possible classes of digrams (for example, in a binary sequence there are four such classes: AA, AB, BA, and BB). A second-order estimate of H is then obtained by taking the difference between $\hat{H}$ (digram) and $\hat{H}_1$:

$$\hat{H}_2 = \hat{H} \text{ (digram)} - \hat{H}_1$$

The rationale of this operation is illustrated schematically in Figure 2. Successive symbols of the sequence are represented by overlapping ellipses; the overlap is intended to indicate

---

† A circumflex over H, thus, "$\hat{H}$," will indicate that the value is an estimate obtained by the use of empirical proportions (symbolized $\hat{p}$), rather than from "true" or a priori probabilities (symbolized p). The importance of this distinction will be discussed in the following chapter, but the reader need not concern himself with it at this point.

that each symbol shares information with those on either side—that is, the symbols are not independent. Now, H_1 is the informational content of a symbol considered independently of preceding symbols. The information in a digram is at least as great as H_1, the information in the first member of the pair.

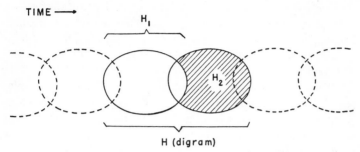

FIG. 2. Successive events, overlapping in information content.

H_2, the amount by which H (digram) exceeds H_1, represents the *new* information contributed by the second member of the pair. But, since every member of the sequence (except the first) is the second member of *some* pair, H_2 may be conceived more generally as the new information added by each symbol in the sequence—new, that is, in the restricted sense that it was not contained in the immediately preceding symbol.

It may be, however, that a knowledge of the *two* symbols preceding a given symbol will increase its predictability (that is, decrease the amount of new information it contains) still further. A third-order estimate is calculated in a manner entirely analogous to that discussed above:

$$\hat{H}_3 = \hat{H} \text{ (trigram)} - \hat{H} \text{ (digram)}$$

If the reader remains unclear as to exactly what is being done here, he should think of the trigram as consisting of a single symbol preceded by a digram. The new information contributed by the terminal symbol is determined by subtracting the content of the initial digram from that of the whole trigram.

Generalizing, we arrive inductively at the formula

$$\hat{H}_N = \hat{H} \text{ (N-gram)} - \hat{H} \overline{(N-1\text{-gram})} \tag{7}$$

where $\quad \hat{H} \text{ (N-gram)} = \Sigma \hat{p} \text{ (N-gram)} \log \dfrac{1}{\hat{p} \text{ (N-gram)}} \tag{8}$

The question arises: How high an order of redundancy must we take into account in order to obtain a reasonably accurate estimate of the net value of H? In theory, no general answer is possible, since a sequence *may* contain patterning of any order whatsoever. Practically, however, two answers are possible. First, it is often the case that $\hat{H}_N$ approaches an asymptote, or stops decreasing altogether, as N is increased. Second, it is simply impractical to compute $\hat{H}_N$ for very high values of N, computational labor being proportional to the Nth power of the number of alternative symbols.

We shall now work through a computational example, calculating estimates of H_1, H_2, H_3, and H_4 for a binary sequence. Suppose that a subject is required (perhaps in an ESP setting) to guess at some random sequence—say, the drawing of black and white balls from the classic urn which contains many such balls in equal proportions. At no time during the guessing is he told whether he is right or wrong. It is well known that sequences of guesses made under such circumstances deviate markedly from randomness, even when the subject deliberately tries to give them a random structure. A sequence of 203 guesses might take some form such as the following:†

```
W B W W B B B W B W B B W W W B B B W W B B W B B B W W
B B W B B W W W B W W B B W W B W W W W B W W W B B W W
W B W W B B W W B W W B B B W W B W W B B B B W W B W W
W W B B B W B W B W W W B W W W B B W B W W B W W W B W
W W W B B W W B W W W B B W W B B B W W W B W B B W W B
W B B W W W B W W B B W W B B W W B B W W W B B W W B
B W B B W W B B B W W B B W B B W W B B W W W B W W B B
W W B B B B B W . . .
```

Instead of proceeding in a "logical" order to tabulate first-order frequencies first, digram frequencies second, etc., we shall find it economical of effort to start out by tabulating N-grams of the highest order (four, in the present example) for which we intend to estimate H. The $2^4 = 16$ possible classes of tetragrams are listed in the extreme left column of Table 1. The next column, headed n_i, shows the frequency

---

† These data are fictitious. However, guessing sequences of the sort described have been studied in considerable detail by Senders [76, 77], using both the method illustrated above and autocorrelation.

TABLE 1

Tetragram	n_i	$n_i \log n_i$
WWWW	3	4.755
WWWB	16	64.000
WWBW	15	58.603
WWBB	24	110.039
WBWW	16	64.000
WBWB	4	8.000
WBBW	22	98.108
WBBB	9	28.529
BWWW	16	64.000
BWWB	23	104.042
BWBW	4	8.000
BWBB	7	19.651
BBWW	23	104.042
BBWB	7	19.651
BBBW	9	28.529
BBBB	2	2.000
Sum	200	785.949

Trigram	n_i	$n_i \log n_i$
WWW	19	80.711
WWB	39	206.131
WBW	20	86.439
WBB	31	153.580
BWW	39	206.131
BWB	11	38.054
BBW	30	147.207
BBB	11	38.054
Sum	200	956.307

Digram	n_i	$n_i \log n_i$
WW	58	339.763
WB	51	289.294
BW	50	282.193
BB	41	219.660
Sum	200	1130.910

Symbol	n_i	$n_i \log n_i$
W	109	737.732
B	91	592.209
Sum	200	1329.941

$\hat{H}(\text{tetragram})$
$= 7.644 - \dfrac{1}{200} \times 785.949$
$= 3.71$

$\hat{H}(\text{trigram})$
$= 7.644 - \dfrac{1}{200} \times 956.307$
$= 2.862$

$\hat{H}(\text{digram})$
$= 7.644 - \dfrac{1}{200} \times 1130.910$
$= 1.989$

$\hat{H}_1 = \log n - \dfrac{1}{n} \sum n_i \log n_i$
$= \log 200 - \dfrac{1}{200} \times 1329.941$
$= 7.644 - 6.649$
$= .995$

$\hat{H}_4 = \hat{H}(\text{tetragram}) - H(\text{trigram})$
$= 3.714 - 2.862$
$= .852$

$\hat{H}_3 = \hat{H}(\text{trigram}) - \hat{H}(\text{digram})$
$= 2.862 - 1.989$
$= .873$

$\hat{H}_2 = \hat{H}(\text{digram}) - \hat{H}_1$
$= 1.989 - .995$
$= .994$

with which each occurs in the sequence. Note that we tabulate *overlapping* tetragrams—the first in the sequence is W B W W, the second B W W B, the third W W B B, and so on; the string of 203 guesses contains 200 such overlapping groups of four. A convenient device to use in tabulating is a small mask, with a slot four symbols wide, which may be moved over the sequence to expose one tetragram at a time. As each tetragram appears, it is tallied in its appropriate class.

Ignore the "$n_i \log n_i$" column for the moment, and note the eight classes of trigrams listed next. The frequency for each trigram is obtained simply by combining the frequencies of the two tetragrams which begin with that trigram (for example, $3 + 16 = 19$, $15 + 24 = 39$, etc.). Likewise, digram frequencies are obtained by combining pairs of trigram frequencies and symbol frequencies by combining digram frequencies. The error which this procedure involves in the treatment of the last three symbols of the sequence may be dismissed as negligible.

Now, in order to find $\hat{H} = \sum \hat{p}_i \log \dfrac{1}{\hat{p}_i}$ for any N-gram, we could obviously divide each n_i by the total $n = 200$ to convert it into a proportion or estimated probability, determine the value of $\hat{p}_i \log \dfrac{1}{\hat{p}_i}$ for each such proportion, and summate. It is actually unnecessary to convert the n_i's into $\hat{p}_i$'s, however, just as it is unnecessary to convert raw scores into deviations from the mean in calculating a variance estimate. If we substitute $\dfrac{n_i}{n}$ for $\hat{p}_i$ in the formula $\hat{H} = \sum \hat{p}_i \log \dfrac{1}{\hat{p}_i}$, and simplify, we obtain

$$H = \log n - \frac{1}{n} \Sigma n_i \log n_i \dagger \qquad (9)$$

---

† If we wish to be more explicit, at the expense of cluttering the formula up slightly, we should write:

$$\hat{H}(x) = \log n - \frac{1}{n} \sum^{i} n(x_i) \log n(x_i).$$

This states what is taken for granted above: that the n_i's employed are those associated with the set of symbols (or N-grams) for which H is being estimated. For H_1, the n_i's are symbol frequencies; for H (digram), they are digram frequencies, and so on.

Again: values of H_N do not tell us what *kind* of guessing pattern the subject is using. An inspection of the tetragram frequencies gives us considerable insight in this respect, however. It appears that the subject has avoided sequences which are "too regular," according to his concept of randomness— namely, long runs of the same event and simple alternations.

The above method of analysis was originated by Miller and Frick [57] in an article, published in 1949, which marked the introduction of information measurement into the literature of psychology. Miller and Frick indicate the broad potentialities of this method for the quantification of patterning or stereotypy in response sequences, wherever responses are confined to a few definite alternatives. In a second article, Frick and Miller [28] use the method to analyze the behavior of a rat in a Skinner-box, the alternative responses being in this case (1) bar pressing, and (2) approach to the food dish.

One of the more interesting subsequent applications of the method has been that of Leary, Harlow, Settlage, and Greenwood [46] to the performance of normal and brain-injured monkeys on double alternation problems. H_N was plotted against N (as in our Figure 3) for four monkeys with frontal lesions, four with posterior lesions, and four normals. Animals of both the posterior and normal groups yielded functions which decreased steadily from $N = 0$ to $N = 4$, indicating sequential dependencies with a range of at least four responses. For the monkeys with frontal lesions, however, the function was horizontal from $N = 1$ to $N = 4$; that is, their responses showed no patterning in time whatever, only certain first-order preferences.

H_N may be given an unambiguous interpretation only when the sequence analyzed has the property of ergodicity discussed at the beginning of this section. For example, if a subject employed one guessing pattern over half of a sequence, and then switched to an entirely different pattern for the second half, the meaning of an $\hat{H}_N$ obtained from the sequence would be at best unclear. This is not to say that any deviation from ergodicity renders the Miller-Frick method totally invalid. Particularly in the case of a learning experiment, in which

This computational formula is one of a group worked out by W. J. McGill [52, 53]. Its usefulness in reducing both labor and error is particularly apparent when n has a value less convenient than the present 200.

Values of $n_i \log n_i$ are obtained from a table which is given in an appendix to this book. For each order of estimation, the sum of these values is entered into formula (9) to obtain an estimate of H (N-gram). $\hat{H}_2$, $\hat{H}_3$, and $\hat{H}_4$ are found by the further use of formula (7). The resulting estimates (together with H_0, which is known a priori to be 1.00) are shown graphically in Figure 3. Through the first two orders analyzed, we

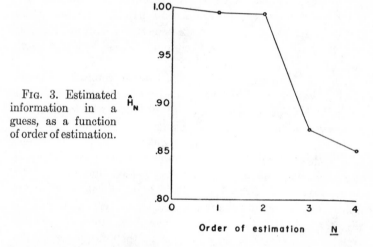

FIG. 3. Estimated information in a guess, as a function of order of estimation.

find very little deviation from randomness, since neither symbol nor digram frequencies are disproportionate to any great extent. At $N = 3$, however, a sharp drop occurs, indicating that a knowledge of the two guesses which have just occurred reduces considerably the uncertainty of the next. Knowing the previous three guesses ($N = 4$) reduces uncertainty somewhat further to a value of .852 bits per symbol; since $H_0 = 1.00$, we may say that redundancy amounts to about 15 percent at the fourth order. Would a fifth-order analysis reveal further patterning? It is suggested that the reader work through such an analysis as an exercise, beginning by tabulating the frequency of each of the 32 possible pentagrams.

patterns emerged during a sequence of responses without changing qualitatively, the *form* of the $\hat{H}_N$ vs. N function would be meaningful even if the absolute values were not. A similar issue is involved in the pooling of subjects. If averaging is desired, it is generally advisable to analyze separately the responses of each subject and then obtain a mean for each $\hat{H}_N$, since different subjects may have very different response patterns. However, a value of $\hat{H}$ based upon the pooled responses of a number of subjects may be interpreted as the average uncertainty involved in predicting individual responses by group laws. This issue will be greatly clarified in the next chapter, when we consider McGill's method for the multivariate analysis of transmitted information.

Thus far nothing has been said about the reliability or significance of information measures. In connection with the guessing-sequence example, one might question the significance of various aspects of the results: whether anything about the sequence differs significantly from chance, whether a knowledge of the three (or two, or one) preceding guesses significantly increases the predictability of a given guess, whether a guess is significantly more predictable from three preceding guesses than from two, etc., etc. Any of these questions is answerable by means of some appropriate χ^2 test. Suppose we wish to test the null hypothesis that there are no sequential dependencies within the range studied; that is, that probabilities contingent upon the three preceding symbols are actually no different from first-order probabilities. If this hypothesis were true, we would expect any pair of tetragrams differing only in the last symbol, such as WWWW and WWWB, to have frequencies proportional to the first-order frequencies of W and B (109 and 91, respectively), within limits of sampling error. The "Expected" frequencies listed in Table 2 are thus apportioned between the tetragrams of each such pair. χ^2 is calculated by the familiar $\dfrac{(O - E)^2}{E}$ formula. The value obtained, 37.5, has 7 degrees of freedom (since we are essentially working with a 2×8 contingency table), and is significant well beyond the .001 level.

TABLE 2

Tetragram	Observed n_i	Expected n_i	$O - E$	$\dfrac{(O - E)^2}{E}$
WWWW	3	10.3	7.3	5.20
WWWB	16	8.7	7.3	6.14
WWBW	15	21.2	6.2	1.81
WWBB	24	17.8	6.2	2.16
WBWW	16	10.9	5.1	2.38
WBWB	4	9.1	5.1	2.86
WBBW	22	16.9	5.1	1.54
WBBB	9	14.1	5.1	1.84
BWWW	16	21.2	5.2	1.27
BWWB	23	17.8	5.2	1.52
BWBW	4	6.0	2.0	.67
BWBB	7	5.0	2.0	.80
BBWW	23	16.3	6.7	2.75
BBWB	7	13.7	6.7	3.28
BBBW	9	6.0	3.0	1.50
BBBB	2	5.0	3.0	1.80

$$\chi^2 = 37.52$$
$$\text{df} = (8 - 1)(2 - 1) = 7$$

In informational terminology: we have just rejected the hypothesis that H_4 is no different from H_1. The difference between H_4 and H_1 may be thought of as the amount by which three consecutive symbols reduce the uncertainty of the one following, or as the amount of information which a given symbol shares with the three preceding it. Letting T stand for this shared information,

$$\hat{T} = \hat{H}_1 - \hat{H}_4 = .995 - .852 = .143$$

Now, there is a very simple relationship between $\hat{T}$ (the estimate of shared information) and χ^2 (the measure of the significance of this estimate), as follows:

$$\chi^2 \cong 2(\log_e 2)\, n\hat{T} = 1.3863\, n\hat{T} \qquad (10)$$

Substituting $n = 200$ and $\hat{T} = .143$, we obtain a χ^2 value of 39.6, which is fairly close to the value 37.5 obtained with the $\dfrac{(O - E)^2}{E}$ formula. The use of formula (10) is a highly economical alternative to the conventional process of calculation illustrated in Table 2, but values so estimated conform only approximately to the χ^2 distribution (as the discrepancy noted above suggests), and should therefore be interpreted with a measure of caution in marginal cases.

Let us use this short-cut formula to test one other difference, the decrease found between $\hat{H}_3$ and $\hat{H}_4$. Do three preceding symbols reduce uncertainty significantly more than two? Since $\hat{H}_3 - \hat{H}_4 = .873 - .852 = .021$, we have

$$\chi^2 \cong 1.3863 \times 200 \times .021 = 5.82$$

Determination of the degrees of freedom involved here requires some thought. We are dealing with what might be called a partial χ^2, testing the independence of the first and last symbols of a tetragram with the intervening pair held constant. For each particular state of the intervening pair, the test would involve a 2×2 contingency table with df $= 1$; since there are four such independent tables (one for each of the four middle digrams WW, WB, BW, and BB), there are four degrees of freedom in all. A χ^2 of 5.82 with df $= 4$ involves a level of confidence between .2 and .3; therefore we conclude that the difference between $\hat{H}_3$ and $\hat{H}_4$ might easily have come about by chance.

The Miller-Frick method of analysis may be applied, with no conceptual difficulty, to sequences involving any number of alternatives. In practice, however, its use has been limited almost entirely to binary sequences. As the number of alternatives is increased, the amount of computational labor required goes up geometrically. For a sequence of events with m alternatives there are m^2 classes of digrams, m^3 classes of trigrams, and in general m^n classes of N-grams. Consider what would be involved in the application of the method to a sequence of letters and spaces making up English text: there could be 27 first-order classifications, $27^2 = 729$ digram classifications, $27^3 = 19,683$ trigram classifications, and so on *ad astra*. The practical limitations thus imposed are unfortunate, because the statistical structure of language is a particularly attractive object of study, as we have seen.

Shannon [78] devised a way around this difficulty with characteristic ingenuity. His method for estimating the redundancy of English "exploits the fact that anyone speaking a language possesses, implicitly, an enormous knowledge of the statistics of the language. Familiarity with the words, idioms, clichés, and grammar enables him to fill in missing or incorrect letters in proof reading, or to complete an unfinished phrase in conversation." Using passages of literary English as material, he had a subject guess the identity of each successive letter. In guessing the first letter of the passage, the subject had nothing to go on but first-order letter probabilities, but as he continued to discover successive letters (and spaces) the guessing became easier: that is, the uncertainty of the Nth letter, H_N, decreased as N increased. When the subject's first guess at a given letter was wrong, he was required to continue guessing until he was right. Thus it was possible to record, for each letter in the passage, the number of guesses required by the subject to identify it.

"A typical result with this experiment is shown below," writes Shannon. "The first line is the original text and the numbers in the second line indicate the guess at which the correct letter was obtained."

```
T H E R E   I S   N O   R E V E R S E   O N   A   M O T O R C Y C L E
1 1 1 5 1 1 2 1 1   2 1 1 1 5 1 1 7 1 1 1 2 1 3   2 1 2 2   7 1 1 1 1 4 1 1 1 1 1
```

```
A   F R I E N D   O F   M I N E   F O U N D   T H I S   O U T
3 1 8 6 1 3 1   1 1 1 1 1 1 1   1 1 1 6 2 1   1 1 1 1   1 2 1 1 1 1 1 1
```

```
R A T H E R   D R A M A T I C A L L Y   T H E   O T H E R   D A Y
4 1 1 1 1   1 1 1 1 5 1   1 1 1 1 1 1 1 1 1 1 6   1 1 1 1 1   1 1 1 1 1 1 1
```

The success of Shannon's subject is impressive: "Out of 102 symbols the subject guessed right on the first guess 79 times, on the second guess 8 times, on the third guess 3 times, the fourth and fifth guesses 2 each, and only eight times required more than five guesses."

What is important about such a record of guesses (though not immediately obvious) is that the sequence of numbers describing the subject's performance may be considered an *encoded version* of the English text, preserving all the information of the original passage. Suppose (suggests Shannon) that the subject had an exact double—an identical twin so completely identical that the two could always be depended upon to make precisely the same guess, given the same material on which to base a guess. Now imagine a communication system in which one of the twins served as an encoder at the transmitting end, and the other as a decoder at the receiving end. Twin A would guess his way through the text of a message in the manner described above. For each letter of the message, a number from 1 to 27 would be transmitted telling how many guesses he required to identify the letter. From these numbers, Twin B could reconstruct the entire message. They would tell him when to *stop* guessing at each letter: for example, "1" would mean "It's the letter you'd consider most probable," "5" would mean "It's the letter that would be your fifth guess," and so on.

Such a sequence of numbers, then, constitutes a "reduced text" in which the statistical structure of the original is greatly simplified. Roughly speaking, this simplification consists of transforming higher orders of redundancy (that is, sequential dependencies) into first-order redundancy, which is highly apparent in the disproportionately large number of 1's and other low numbers of guesses, and the rareness of high numbers. If the reduced text involves only first-order redundancy, it would seem legitimate to evaluate its informational content by the formula $H = \sum\limits^{27} p_i \log \dfrac{1}{p_i}$, the p_i's being in this case the proportion of times each number from 1 through 27 appears. The objection to applying this formula to the reduced text of a single passage, like that illustrated above, is that the sequence of numbers is necessarily nonergodic, since guessing becomes more accurate as more letters are discovered.

What is needed, instead, is a separate set of proportions for each number of letters preceding the letter guessed. Such a set will be called N-gram proportions when they pertain to the prediction of the Nth letter of a passage. Corresponding values of H_N may then be estimated (or rather bracketed, as we shall presently see). As in the case of the Miller-Frick method, H_N is an Nth-order measure of information; that is, the average uncertainty of a letter when the $N - 1$ preceding letters are known, or the average amount of new information in the Nth letter of a sequence. In order to obtain fairly stable proportions for N-grams from $N = 1$ to $N = 15$, Shannon had a subject guess through one hundred passages of 15 letters each. He then compiled a separate frequency distribution (that is, frequency with which each number of guesses from 1 to 27 was required to identify the correct letter) for each of the 15 letters, pooling across the 100 passages. In addition, he obtained a distribution for $N = 100$ by having his subject predict only the last letter of a passage 100 letters in length; this also was done with 100 passages. The improvement in guessing with knowledge of past letters may be illustrated by reproducing the first row of Shannon's table, which gives the frequency of 1's (correct on first guess) for successive N-grams: 18, 29, 36, 47, 51, 58, 48, 66, 66, 67, 62, 58, 66, 72, 60 (for $N = 15$), and 80 (for $N = 100$).

The formula $\sum \hat{p}_i \log \dfrac{1}{\hat{p}_i}$ may be applied to any set of N-gram proportions to yield an estimate of H_N which actually constitutes an *upper limit* to the true value. The reason why this is an upper bound rather than an unbiased estimate is not too difficult to see. We know, by the line of reasoning presented earlier, that reduced text may be considered an encoded version of the original; hence the first-order uncertainty of the reduced text (for any particular value of N) must be at least as great as H_N, the Nth-order uncertainty of the original text. It may be somewhat greater, because the transformation of higher orders of redundancy into first-order redundancy which occurs in going from original to reduced text is not perfect. The loose-jointedness of this transformation is attributable to the fact that even a hypothetically ideal subject, in guessing at a particular letter, does not reveal in his guesses (or need to know) any exact distribution of probabilities for the next letter, but only the *order* of certain of these probabilities.

By a mathematical argument which will not be recapitulated here, Shannon obtains also an expression describing the lower bound of H_N. The two formulas which bracket H_N are:

Upper bound:

$$H_N = \sum_{i=1}^{i=27} \hat{p}_i^N \log \frac{1}{\hat{p}_i^N}, \quad \text{and} \tag{11}$$

Lower bound:

$$H_N = \sum_{i=1}^{i=27} (\hat{p}_i^N - \hat{p}_{i+1}^N) i \log i \tag{12}$$

in which $\hat{p}_i^N$ stands for the proportion of times i guesses are required to identify the Nth letter of a passage. It is likely that the upper bound so calculated is closer to the true value of H_N than is the lower bound. In order for H_N actually to be as low as indicated in formula (12), this highly implausible condition must be satisfied: whenever a letter is to be predicted, there must be a set of possible next letters all of equal probability, while all other next letters have zero probability. Figure 4 is a graph of Shannon's results, showing how the uncertainty of a letter in English text decreases as the length of the preceding passage is increased. Of particular interest are the bounds for $N = 100$ (upper, 1.3; lower, .6), since these may be very close to the asymptotic values which would be obtained with indefinitely long passages. It appears that in a long passage of English text, for example a novel, the average amount of new information contributed by a letter must settle down to something like one bit, or possibly less. This is in contrast to the log 27 = 4.76 bits which each letter would contain if all the symbols were equally likely and no sequential dependencies

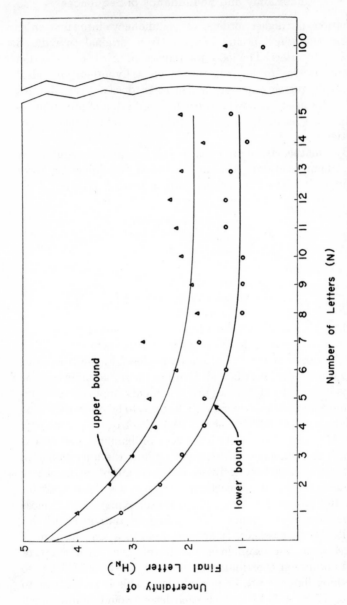

FIG. 4. Results of Shannon's guessing-game experiment; uncertainty of the last letter in a sequence N letters long.

existed. Thus a conservative estimate of the redundancy of English is about 75 percent.

From the fact that everything is in effect repeated about three times in English, it does not follow that we should enthusiastically set about to pare the language down for greater efficiency. Redundancy is a powerful safeguard against error and misunderstanding in communication: if the language were completely nonredundant, every typographical error would result in a sentence which made sense, but a sense different from that intended by the author. It has been demonstrated by Miller, Heise, and Lichten [58], that the intelligibility of speech heard against a background of noise is dependent upon the redundancy of the verbal material spoken. Words are understood better than nonsense syllables through noise of a given level (or as well through more noise); likewise words in sentences are understood better than the same words in isolation. Intelligibility also increases as the number of alternative words in the test vocabulary is decreased—that is, as the informational content of each word is decreased.

Before discussing further applications and potentialities of Shannon's guessing-game technique, let us take a brief look at an alternative method devised by Newman and Gerstman [61] for finding an upper bound to H_N. These authors suggest a new informational statistic which may be symbolized D_N, called the *coefficient of constraint*. D_N is the average information shared by two symbols $N - 1$ places apart in a sequence, expressed as a proportion of the first-order informational content of a symbol, H_1. It may be thought of, in terms slightly more concrete, as that proportion of the information in a symbol which is predicted by the symbol $N - 1$ places before it, ignoring all intervening symbols. D_N resembles a correlation coefficient to the extent that a value of 0 indicates that the two symbols are independent, and a value of 1.00 that either is completely predictable from the other. A mathematical definition may be expressed in any one of several ways:

$$D_N = \frac{T(i; i + N - 1)}{H_1} \qquad (13a)$$

in which $T(i; i + N - 1)$ is the information shared by symbol i and symbol $(i + N - 1)$; or

$$D_N = 1 - \frac{H_i(i + N - 1)}{H_1} \qquad (13b)$$

in which $H_i(i + N - 1)$ is the remaining uncertainty of $(i + N - 1)$ when i is known; or in terms most convenient for computational purposes,

$$\hat{D}_N = \frac{2\hat{H}_1 - \hat{H} \text{ (digram } i, i + N - 1)}{\hat{H}_1}$$

$$= 2 - \frac{\hat{H} (i, i + N - 1)}{\hat{H}_1} \qquad (13c)$$

$\hat{H}(i, i + N - 1)$ is simply an estimate of the (digram) information in pairs of symbols $N - 1$ places apart in the sequence. It is calculated in precisely the same manner as $\hat{H}$(digram) by the Miller-Frick method, but the symbols considered in pairs are no longer adjacent except when $N = 2$.

Newman and Gerstman suggest the following formula for obtaining an upper bound to H_N:

$$H_N \lessgtr (1 - D_N) \cdot H_{N-1} \qquad (14)$$

If this formula is considered as an equality, it proposes "That the coefficient of constraint be regarded as a proportion by which the amount of information per letter is successively reduced as the constraining sequence is made longer and longer." The basic assumption underlying this proposal may be clarified somewhat as follows. Designating any two symbols located $N - 1$ places apart as a and c, and the whole group of intervening symbols as b, the assumption is that, if a knowledge of a reduces the informational content of c by a given proportion (D_N), then a will likewise reduce that component of the information in c which is not shared with b [that is, $H_b(c)$] by the same proportion. In other words, it is assumed that the *pattern* of a and b is unimportant; that these symbols do not interact in placing a constraint upon c. In the case of language sequences this assumption is almost certainly false, since the predictability of successive letters seems to depend to a considerable degree upon the pattern (as well as the separate identities) of preceding letters. It is for this reason that the expression in (14) constitutes an upper bound, rather than an unbiased estimate, of H_N.

By means of an automatic tabulator operated by teletypewriter tape, Newman and Gerstman analyzed a 10,000-letter sample of printed English taken from the Bible. They calculated $\hat{D}_N$ for six values of N: 2, 3, 4, 5, 6, and 10. A beautifully simple function was found to describe the results with great accuracy:

$$\hat{D}_N = \frac{1}{N^2}$$

From this empirical equation and formula (14), an upper bound for H_N was obtained at each of the values of N which Shannon had investigated. These upper bounds tend to be lower than Shannon's upper-bound values for small values of N (<5) and higher for large values, with an asymptote at 2.04 bits. The agreement with Shannon's curve is at least as good as one would expect, in view of the fact that the two curves constitute upper bounds for entirely different reasons.

The most important similarities and differences among the three methods of analysis which have been described in this section may be summarized as follows. All have the general aim of determining the degree to which a sequence is redundant —that is, the degree to which the informational content of a symbol is reduced by unequal symbol probabilities and by sequential dependencies of various orders. This is accomplished by estimating values for H_N, the average amount of new information conveyed by a symbol when the preceding $N - 1$ symbols are known. The Miller-Frick method is entirely objective, and yields estimates of H_N which are accurate except for sampling error (though we shall see in the next chapter that this sampling error contains a constant bias, as well as a variable component). The disadvantage of the method is simply that it becomes computationally impossible for sequences involving many alternatives and long-range sequential dependencies. The Newman-Gerstman method is also entirely objective, and requires no more computation at any value of N than the Miller-Frick method requires at $N = 2$. This saving is achieved by ignoring patterning or interaction effects, with the result that calculated values of H_N will exceed true values to some unknown degree dependent upon the importance of interaction in the sequence. Autocorrelational analysis (which is not considered in this book) likewise ignores interaction effects, but autocorrelation may be applied only to sequences in which the alternatives are either binary or ordered along a continuum, whereas the Newman-Gerstman method is not restricted in any such way. Shannon's guessing-game method requires a great deal of experimental work but relatively little subsequent computation, regardless of the value of N; it takes interaction effects into account, and yields a lower as well as an upper bound to H_N. The most conspicuous singularity of the method is its use of the memory of a human organism as a source of data concerning the structural characteristics of language sequences. This "subjective" aspect of Shannon's method deserves a more careful examination than we have yet given it.

It is necessary for Shannon to assume that his subject's implicit knowledge of the statistical properties of English is practically perfect. One would like, however, to have some criterion by which to decide when such an assumption is justified. Suppose (to take as an example an unexplored area in which informational analysis should yield interesting results) we wished to study sequential dependencies in music. Might we reasonably use the guessing-game technique with a trained musician as subject? If we did, and obtained higher values of H for Schoenberg's music than for Mozart's, would this mean that Mozart's music is actually the more lawful, or merely that Schoenberg's rules were not as well imbedded in the nervous system of our subject? Returning to the area of language: I have found that naive subjects' judgments of first-order letter probabilities correspond only in a very rough way to objective first-order probabilities [3]. Shannon's subject was undoubtedly more sophisticated than those in my study, and in addition was supplied with tables of letter, digram, and trigram frequencies; nevertheless, the amount of discrepancy between this subject's higher-order predictions and "ideal" prediction remains a matter for speculation.

Although the validity of such predictions is virtually impossible to check (since by *validity* we mean not predictive accuracy, but rather the extent to which predictions are based upon valid or objectively accurate probabilities), their reliability can and should be studied. If a number of subjects independently guessing through the same passage did not agree with one another guess for guess, it would be necessary to conclude that at least some of them were basing their guesses upon somewhat imperfect subjective probabilities. In such a case, it would be clearly advantageous to calculate H_N from some consensus of judgment. This could be accomplished by a slight variation of Shannon's procedure. At every step in the passage, each subject would list all the letters of the alphabet which might reasonably occur in the next place, in the order of their probability, and only after this ordering of all the possibilities would he be told which was correct. A mean rank would subsequently be calculated, over all subjects, for each of the letters listed as a possibility. The ordinal position of the mean rank of the correct letter would be considered the number of guesses required by the group (as a hypothetical democratic body) to predict the letter in question. It seems fairly certain that a value of H_N estimated from such group guesses would be more accurate, and somewhat lower, than the H_N from a typical individual subject.†

What we are concerned with above is the obvious possibility that calculated values (or, rather, brackets) of H_N will be too high because of the subject's incomplete appreciation of statistical regularities which are objectively present. On the other hand, there is the less obvious possibility that a subject's guesses may, in a sense, be *too* good. Shannon's intent is presumably to study statistical restraints which pertain to language. But a subject given a long sequence of letters which he has probably *never* encountered before, in that exact pattern, may be expected to base his prediction of the next letter not only upon language statistics, but also upon his general knowledge

---

† Presumably some analogue of the Spearman-Brown relationship (see Guilford [33] p. 421) would hold here.

of the world to which language refers. A possible reply to this criticism is that all but the lowest orders of sequential dependency in language are in any case attributable to natural connections among the referents of words, and that it is entirely legitimate for a human predictor to take advantage of such natural connections to estimate transitional *probabilities* of language, even when no empirical *frequencies* corresponding to the probabilities exist. It is nevertheless important to realize that a human predictor is conceivably superior to a hypothetical "ideal predictor" who knows none of the connections between words and their referents, but who (with unlimited computational facilities) has analyzed all the English ever written and discovered all the statistical regularities residing therein.

The faults we find with Shannon's guessing game as a technique for studying sequences become advantages when we consider its potentialities as a technique for studying subjects. Over a wide range of psychological experiments, the experimenter requires the subject to choose one of several alternatives (which may be either explicit or understood) in order to find out how much he knows, or has observed or learned. Suppose there are ten alternative responses, one of which is "correct," and the subject makes an incorrect response. Ordinarily the experimenter merely records this as an error, and does not inquire how great the subject's uncertainty actually was: whether he was at a complete loss, and chose one of the ten alternatives capriciously, or whether he was able to reject eight alternatives and still chose the wrong one of the two between which he was undecided. The Shannon procedure of allowing the subject to guess until he is right provides a much finer measure of performance (literally, it gives the experimenter more information about the subject), with the result that data have greater stability and hence fewer subjects may be required.

By means of a simple apparatus designed by Dr. M. D. Arnoult and myself, the procedure may be used with subjects in groups. A subject makes a response by punching, with a bevel-pointed stylus, one of a number of alternative positions which are indicated, with suitable labels, on each row of his response sheet. This sheet is rigidly attached to a board in which small holes have been drilled. Under all the wrong alternatives in a row, the holes are filled almost to the top with pins which stop the stylus before it penetrates deeply, whereas under the correct alternative is an unblocked hole which allows the stylus to enter much farther and make a larger hole in the sheet, telling the subject he is right. The number of holes punched in each row thus constitutes a record of the number of guesses required by the subject to determine the correct alternative. Some 50 rows of 8 or more alternatives may easily be presented in this way.

The guessing-game technique has been used to excellent advantage by Pollack [63] in a series of experiments on "the assimilation of sequentially-encoded information." Pollack investigated the amount of information which a subject can reproduce from immediate memory, as a function of such variables as number of alternative symbols and length of sequence. For example, a subject might be read a series of 8 symbols, any one of which might be either a digit or a letter of the alphabet (making a total of 36 alternatives). If the sequence "BX3G9KRF" were read, and the subject responsed by writing "BX3C9RKF," he would be told that his 4th, 6th, and 7th symbols were in error, and allowed to guess at each of them as many times as necessary to correct it. Pollack used Shannon's upper-bound equation (our formula 11) to obtain an estimate of the information lost by (or upon) the subject. Some of the results of these experiments will be mentioned in the following chapter, which will deal with the study of the human organism's characteristics as an information channel.

CHAPTER 3

Man's Ability to Transmit Information

T HAT THE NERVOUS SYSTEM is a complex communications network, that the brain functions as a kind of computer with extensive facilities for storing information, that psychological processes are essentially information-handling operations—this point of view is so widespread today that we are likely to forget how recent it is, and that less than ten years ago it was peculiar to Norbert Wiener, Warren McCulloch, and a handful of other imaginative individuals. Although many psychologists at present argue that other approaches to psychological problems are more productive, few would take the position that this point of view is untenable or erroneous.

The inquiry into man's characteristics as an information-handling mechanism has already generated a sizable and steadily growing body of experimental work. In this chapter we shall consider two general questions which have accounted for a large part of this experimentation. The first of these to arise, which seems to have occurred to many people simultaneously after reading Shannon and Wiener, has to do with the maximum rate at which a human being, functioning as a link in a communications system, can transmit information. What is the greatest number of binary-decisions-per-second possible for an individual, and under what conditions may the maximum number be achieved? One would expect this maximum to be represented in such highly practiced activities as reading and piano playing; the unique advantage of information theory is that it enables us to measure such superficially diverse activities in comparable terms.

The second question—or cluster of questions—has to do with the quantity of information that may be conveyed to an observer by means of a single stimulus dimension, or by means of several such dimensions in controlled combination. Given some stimulus continuum such as length, or brightness, or pitch, how many alternative values along the continuum may function as "code symbols" for an observer—that is, how many values can he identify unequivocally, without the use of any objective yardstick? Are some stimulus dimensions appreciably better as information carriers than others? Is there any simple relationship between the range of stimuli in j.n.d.'s and the amount of information they convey to an observer? Do stimuli which vary on two dimensions convey twice as much information as stimuli which vary on only one? It is from this second group of questions that we shall launch the discussion to follow, since this issue has a certain rational priority over the matter of time rates, and besides involves some extremely important methodological advances of which the reader should learn immediately.

Multivariate Informational Analysis

The idea of measuring in informational terms the accuracy of stimulus identification, together with a simple technique for doing so, was first suggested in 1951 by Garner and Hake, in an article titled "The amount of information in absolute judgments" [31]. The Garner-Hake method opened a whole new area of experimentation and further provided the basis for McGill's [52, 53] development of a method of multivariate analysis which is the informational analogue of analysis of variance components. In the following account, I shall to some extent telescope the contributions of Garner and Hake with those of McGill, using McGill's symbolism and computational formulas from the beginning.

Consider an experiment in which the subject is successively shown various stimuli of a class and is required to identify each, by some "name," when it appears. It will be assumed that the subject has already practiced at this task until his performance is at an asymptote. It will also be assumed, for the sake of being definite, that the stimuli are ordered along some continuum (for example, they might be Munsell gray patches, varying in brightness; or squares, varying in area), but this assumption is entirely irrelevant to the computations we shall perform—the stimuli might equally well be odors, for which no dimensional organization is known. Likewise, we shall take an example in which every stimulus has a unique response—some name or some number which is "correct"—so that the number of stimulus categories and the number of response categories are equal. The method to be described, however, applies equally well to situations in which this equality does not obtain; an experiment might, for example, employ a hundred different stimuli, but require only that the subject assign each to one of six response categories. In any case, the experimenter will always record the particular response made by the subject when a particular stimulus is presented—not merely whether or not the response is correct.

Now, the information *presented* to the subject (per stimulus exposure) is easy enough to calculate: if the various stimuli are presented equally often (as is customarily the case) it is simply the log of the number of stimulus alternatives (formula 1). Our problem is to determine how much of this information is actually conveyed or *transmitted* to the subject, and how much is lost. Or, to turn the question about: if we know only what the subject *says* a stimulus was, how great is our remaining uncertainty as to what it actually was?

In order to attack this problem, we must first establish an orderly system for classifying our data and for symbolizing the various quantities with which we shall be dealing.† The frequency with which each response is made to each stimulus is recorded in a table the columns of which represent alternative stimuli and the rows of which represent alternative responses (see Table 3). The alternative stimuli, $x_1, x_2 \cdots x_i \cdots X$, may

TABLE 3

		x						
	1	2	$\cdots$	i	$\cdots$	$\cdots$	X	
1	n_{11}	n_{21}	$\cdots$	n_{i1}	$\cdots$	$\cdots$	n_{X1}	$n._1$
2	n_{12}	n_{22}	$\cdots$	n_{i2}	$\cdots$	$\cdots$	n_{X2}	$n._2$
3	n_{13}	n_{23}	$\cdots$	n_{i3}	$\cdots$	$\cdots$	n_{X3}	$n._3$
y $\cdots$	$\cdots$	$\cdots$	$\cdots$	$\cdots$	$\cdots$	$\cdots$	$\cdots$	$\cdots$
j	n_{1j}	n_{2j}	$\cdots$	n_{ij}	$\cdots$	$\cdots$	n_{Xj}	$n._j$
$\cdots$	$\cdots$	$\cdots$	$\cdots$	$\cdots$	$\cdots$	$\cdots$	$\cdots$	$\cdots$
Y	n_{1Y}	n_{2Y}	$\cdots$	n_{iY}	$\cdots$	$\cdots$	n_{XY}	$n._Y$
	$n_1.$	$n_2.$	$\cdots$	$n_i.$	$\cdots$	$\cdots$	$n_X.$	n

thus be thought of as discrete values of the stimulus variable x (even when x is not a continuum); likewise $y_1, y_2 \cdots y_j \cdots Y$ are thought of as discrete values of the response variable y (*upper-case* X and Y stand for the number of stimulus and

† To the reader whose mathematical training is not such as to render this advice officious, let me suggest that he take the pains to understand and assimilate the system of notation now, as it is described, rather than skim over it lightly with the view of referring back when he needs to know what a symbol means. The mathematical operations presently to be described are really very simple, and will appear difficult only if the language in which they are expressed is foreign to the reader.

response categories, respectively). Note that the subscript i is used to refer to any particular but unspecified stimulus, and the subscript j to any particular but unspecified response. The number of times stimulus x_i is presented will be symbolized by $n_i.$ (or simply n_i, when the dot may be omitted without ambiguity), the frequency of response, y_j, by $n._j$ (or simply n_j), and the frequency with which the stimulus x_i evokes the response y_j by n_{ij}. It is immediately obvious from Table 3

(1) that $\qquad \sum^{i} n_{ij} = n_i.$

(2) that $\qquad \sum^{i} n_{ij} = n._j$

(3) and that $\qquad \sum^{i,j} n_{ij} = \sum^{i} n_i. = \sum^{j} n._j = n,$

the total of all frequencies.

If we wished, we could transform all these frequencies into probability estimates, or proportions, merely by dividing through by n (that is, $\hat{p}_{ij} = \dfrac{n_{ij}}{n}$, $\hat{p}_i = \dfrac{n_i.}{n}$, and $\hat{p}._j = \dfrac{n._j}{n}$). This transformation is not necessary for the computation of informational measures, though such measures are more easily defined and conceptualized in terms of probabilities.

Table 4 gives an example of specific frequencies that might be obtained from an experiment in which five alternative stimuli were each presented 50 times to a subject, always in random order. These frequencies will be referred to by means of the symbols given in the preceding table; for example, $n_{32} = 5$, $n._1 = 48$, $n_i. = 50$, and so on. Now, there are three informational quantities that may be calculated directly from a table like this, namely $\hat{H}(x)$, $\hat{H}(y)$, and $\hat{H}(x,y)$:

$$\hat{H}(x) = \sum^{i} \hat{p}_i \log \frac{1}{\hat{p}_i} =$$

$$\text{(with stimuli of equal frequency) } \log X \quad (15)$$

$$\hat{H}(y) = \sum^{i} \hat{p}_i \log \frac{1}{\hat{p}_i} \quad (16)$$

$$\hat{H}(x,y) = \sum^{i,j} \hat{p}_{ij} \log \frac{1}{\hat{p}_{ij}} \quad (17)$$

$\hat{H}(x)$, the estimated information-per-stimulus, and $\hat{H}(y)$, the estimated information-per-response, are obtained from the marginal totals of the table, and should present no difficulty to

TABLE 4

x

	1	2	3	4	5	
1	46	2				48
2	3	44	5			52
y 3	1	4	38	7	1	51
4			6	40	4	50
5			1	3	45	49
	50	50	50	50	50	250

$\hat{H}(y) = 2.322$

$$H(x) = 2.323$$
$$\hat{H}(x,y) = 3.054$$
$$\hat{T}(x;y) = H(x) + \hat{H}(y) - \hat{H}(x,y) = 1.591$$

the reader. $\hat{H}(x,y)$ is slightly less obvious: it is the estimated information in the *joint occurrence* of a stimulus and a response, and is equal to the sum of $\hat{p} \log \hat{p}$ values for all the *cells*. As we saw in the previous chapter, frequencies may be used instead of proportions in estimating the Shannon-Wiener measure of information; thus we may rewrite the above equations as

$$\hat{H}(x) = \log n - \frac{1}{n} \sum^{i} n_i \log n_i \qquad (15a)$$

$$\hat{H}(y) = \log n - \frac{1}{n} \sum^{j} n_j \log n_j \qquad (16a)$$

$$\hat{H}(x,y) = \log n - \frac{1}{n} \sum^{i,j} n_{ij} \log n_{ij} \qquad (17a)$$

For the data given in Table 4,

$H(x) = \log 5 = 2.323$ (since stimuli are equiprobable)

$\hat{H}(y) = \log 250$

$$- \frac{1}{250} (48 \log 48 + 52 \log 52 \cdots \text{etc.}) = 2.322$$

$\hat{H}(x,y) = \log 250$

$$- \frac{1}{250} (46 \log 46 + 2 \log 2 + 3 \log 3 \cdots \text{etc.})$$

$$= 3.054$$

Note that the five alternative responses have so nearly the same frequency that $\hat{H}(y)$ deviates from log 5 by only .001 bits.

From these values of $H(x)$ and $\hat{H}(y)$ it is evident that the subject's judgments contain almost exactly the same *amount* of information as the stimuli judged. This is no way implies, however, that the *information* is the same. Indeed, $\hat{H}(y)$ would still equal $H(x)$ if the subject had completely ignored the stimuli and repeated the five responses over and over in regular succession. In any such case of complete independence between x and y, the amount of information in their joint occurrence, $H(x,y)$, is equal to the sum of their individual information values, $H(x)$ and $H(y)$. On the other hand, if $H(x, y)$ is *less* than $H(x) + H(y)$, we may infer that $H(x)$ and $H(y)$ overlap— that is, that x and y share information. Letting $T(x;y)$ stand for the amount of this shared information, the information *transmitted* from stimulus to response, we may write

$$T(x;y) = H(x) + H(y) - H(x,y) \qquad (18)$$

The reader will recall that T was employed in the previous chapter as a measure of shared or transmitted information, and that it was obtained by a similar subtraction process.

Applying formula (18) to the estimates calculated from Table 4, we have

$$\hat{T}(x;y) = H(x) + \hat{H}(y) - \hat{H}(x,y)$$

$$= 2.323 + 2.322 - 3.045$$

$$= 1.591$$

This is our estimate of the amount of information transmitted by the subject from stimulus to response: 1.59 bits, out of a possible 2.32.

The relationships among $H(x)$, $H(y)$, $H(x,y)$, $T(x;y)$, and two other measures not yet mentioned are shown in Figure 5, by means of a graphical device adopted from Quastler [68].

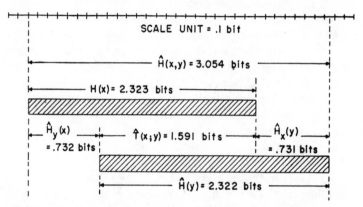

FIG. 5. Relationship between information components in the two-variable case. Adapted from Quastler [52].

$T(x;y)$ is represented as the overlap between $H(x)$ and $H(y)$ within the confines of $H(x,y)$. The two new functions, $H_y(x)$ and $H_x(y)$, may be described thus:

$$H_y(x) = H(x,y) - H(y) = H(x) - T(x;y) \qquad (19)$$

$$H_x(y) = H(x,y) - H(x) = H(y) - T(x;y) \qquad (20)$$

$H_y(x)$, sometimes called the *equivocation* of transmission, is that component of the stimulus information which is lost by the subject; in other words, it is the uncertainty of the stimulus when the response is known, or specified. $H_x(y)$, which is sometimes called *ambiguity*, is the uncertainty of the response, given the stimulus; it may be thought of as the irrelevant or "noise" component of response information. A clear understanding of the foregoing concepts is greatly facilitated by a careful consideration of Figure 5.

Observing what happens to these information functions in several limiting cases serves further to educate one's intuition.

(1) The case in which responses have no relation to stimuli has already been suggested: $H(x) + H(y)$ will exactly equal $H(x,y)$, and $T(x;y)$ will equal zero. $H(x)$ and $H_y(x)$ will be identical; so will $H(y)$ and $H_x(y)$.

(2) In the opposite case of perfect transmission, each stimulus evokes its own unique response. We think most readily of a frequency table in which only the cells on the *diagonal* are occupied, but if the stimuli and responses are not ordered along continua, a pairing of any row with any column may be involved. Moreover, transmission is considered to be perfect even when some or all responses are "wrong" by external standards, provided the subject is perfectly consistent in his "errors," and maintains his own one-to-one correspondences between responses and stimuli. With perfect transmission, $T(x;y) = H(x) = H(y) = H(x,y)$, and $H_y(x) = 0 = H_x(y)$.

(3) Suppose that a subject always gave the *same* response, regardless of the stimulus. In this case $H(y)$ would be zero; so would $T(x;y)$ and $H_x(y)$. $H(x,y)$ and $H_y(x)$ would both equal $H(x)$, x being the only source of uncertainty in the entire situation. Obviously, a subject who really behaved in any such way would never be endured throughout an experimental session. Mild response preferences are not uncommon, but typically $H(y)$ is almost as great as $H(x)$ unless there are so many alternatives that the subject tends to respond in "round numbers," or unless stimulus and response categories have been made unequal in number as part of an experimental design.

The term "transmitted information" suggests some sort of flow from a source to a sink or destination. The use of the term to describe the constraint of stimuli on responses is compatible with this idea of a causal flow. The reader should note, however, that none of the operations employed in calculating $\hat{T}(x;y)$ require any assumption about the direction, or even the existence, of any such causal relationship; that is, $T(x;y)$ is the same as $T(y;x)$. T is a measure of "transmitted information" only by inference, and only in certain situations; more directly it measures *relatedness*, or *association*, or *shared information*.

One may calculate a value of $\hat{T}$ for any contingency table where χ^2 would be an appropriate test of significance—for instance, a frequency table relating color of hair to color of eyes. T is thus similar to the contingency coefficient, C, though it has the advantage of being expressed in a meaningful unit, the bit. It is also similar to the correlation coefficient in that both are measures of relatedness (see Appendix I), but whereas r demands *equal-interval* scaling of the variables involved, T demands only *nominal* scaling (Stevens [81] especially Table II).

So far our discussion of transmitted or shared information has been restricted to the simple case of two variables. We shall now see (following the work of McGill [52, 53]) that the analysis may be extended to deal with as many dimensions as our experimental and computational facilities permit. Consider a frequency table of the sort suggested in Figure 6. This is

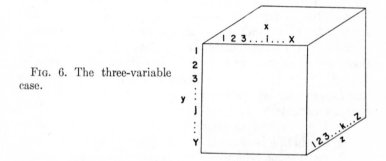

FIG. 6. The three-variable case.

exactly like the earlier table, except that a third dimension, z, with values $1, 2, 3 \cdots k \cdots Z$, has been added. Each cell is now a small cube, containing the frequency n_{ijk} with which some particular combination of values on the three variables has occurred.

Any one of a variety of experimental designs might employ or give rise to three such variables. Here are some possible examples:

(1) If x is the stimulus variable and y the response variable in an identification experiment, as before, z might be *subjects*. The problem of combining results from different subjects, who

may have different constant error patterns, was touched upon briefly in the preceding chapter. By means of the present arrangement it is possible to think of a response as containing information about the subject who makes it, as well as about the stimulus to which it is made, and to isolate these two components from the total response information.

(2) Again, with x as a set of values on some stimulus dimension and y as a set of responses identifying these stimulus values, z might be an additional stimulus dimension which the subject tries to ignore. Suppose, more specifically, that a trained subject attempts to identify, by means of numerical responses, y, the frequency of tones which vary in both frequency, x, and amplitude, z. The present arrangement allows us to analyze the influence of the "irrelevant" variable, amplitude, upon the amount of information conveyed by the primary variable, frequency.

(3) Still letting x be stimuli and y responses, we might study effects of practice by giving successive experimental sessions values on z. This design suggests a generally useful dodge for application to nonergodic sequences: the amount of deviation from ergodicity resulting from such factors as practice and fatigue may be evaluated by treating blocks of trials as a separate variable.

(4) If we wished to study possible *sequential* constraints among identifying responses, we might determine the informational relationships between the present stimulus, x, the present response, y, and the preceding response, z.

(5) The variables in the table need have nothing to do with identification of stimuli at all: z might consist of alternative responses to Gallup's perennial question, "Do you consider yourself a Democrat, a Republican, or an Independent?" with x classifying the occupation, and y the geographical location, of the respondent. Multivariate informational analysis offers the unique advantage of measuring *interaction* among such categorical variables.

The reader may think in terms of any of the preceding examples that most strikes his fancy, if he wishes to give a concrete meaning to x, y, and z in the exposition to follow. Looking again at Figure 6, we see that the rectangular solid representing a trivariate frequency table has three visible surfaces: the front, which may be called xy, the top xz, and the side yz. Now, we may "collapse" the solid onto any one of these surfaces by summing frequencies over the remaining dimension. For example, if we collapse upon the front, or xy, surface, we will collect in each of its square cells the total frequency of all the cubical cells which lie directly behind that square on z. Such surface totals are obtained by collapsing upon each of the three planes in turn. A particular but unspecified cell total on the xy surface is designated n_{ij}, on the xz surface n_{ik}, and on the yz surface n_{jk}. In short, then,

$$n_{ij} = \sum_{k=1}^{k=Z} n_{ijk} \tag{21}$$

$$n_{ik} = \sum_{j=1}^{j=Y} n_{ijk} \tag{22}$$

$$n_{jk} = \sum_{i=1}^{i=X} n_{ijk} \tag{23}$$

Each of the three surfaces thus becomes a two-dimensional frequency table of the sort illustrated earlier in Tables 3 and 4. These surface totals are further summated or collapsed to give totals for each of the three variables singly: for example, the total x frequencies (n_i) are obtained by summing each of the columns of either the top or front surface, the y frequencies (n_j) are row sums from either the front or side, and the z frequencies (n_k) are row sums from the top or column sums from the side. To be mathematically explicit,

$$n_i = \sum^i \sum^k n_{ijk} \tag{24}$$

$$n_j = \sum^i \sum^k n_{ijk} \tag{25}$$

$$n_k = \sum^i \sum^j n_{ijk} \tag{26}$$

We now have seven sets of frequencies: a set for each variable $(n_i, n_j, \text{ and } n_k)$, a set for each *pair* of variables $(n_{ij}, n_{ik}, \text{ and }$

n_{jk}), and the set for all three variables (n_{ijk}) with which we started. An $\hat{H}$ may be calculated for each of these sets by the following formulas, which should contain nothing new to the reader:

$$\hat{H}(x) = \log n - \frac{1}{n} \sum^{i} n_i \log n_i \qquad (27)$$

$$\hat{H}(y) = \log n - \frac{1}{n} \sum^{j} n_j \log n_j \qquad (28)$$

$$\hat{H}(z) = \log n - \frac{1}{n} \sum^{k} n_k \log n_k \qquad (29)$$

$$\hat{H}(x,y) = \log n - \frac{1}{n} \sum^{i,j} n_{ij} \log n_{ij} \qquad (30)$$

$$\hat{H}(x,z) = \log n - \frac{1}{n} \sum^{i,k} n_{ik} \log n_{ik} \qquad (31)$$

$$\hat{H}(y,z) = \log n - \frac{1}{n} \sum^{j,k} n_{jk} \log n_{jk} \qquad (32)$$

$$\hat{H}(x,y,z) = \log n - \frac{1}{n} \sum^{i,j,k} n_{ijk} \log n_{ijk} \qquad (33)$$

Only the last of these, $\hat{H}(x,y,z)$, which is the information associated with cubicle frequencies (and is accordingly the *total* information-per-observation), is any different from the functions that we calculated in the two-variable case (see Table 4). We may think of $\hat{H}(x)$, $\hat{H}(y)$, and $\hat{H}(x,y)$ as describing the front surface of Figure 6; $\hat{H}(x)$, $\hat{H}(z)$, and $\hat{H}(x,z)$ the top surface; and $\hat{H}(y)$, $\hat{H}(z)$, and $\hat{H}(y,z)$ the side surface.

Now the seven $\hat{H}$'s thus calculated may be combined to generate a number of additional functions (23 more, to be exact!) which we shall find quite overwhelming unless we keep our thinking orderly and observe that only a few fundamental concepts and operations are involved. We already know how to determine a value of $\hat{T}$ for each surface [namely, $\hat{T}(x;y)$, $\hat{T}(x;z)$, and $\hat{T}(y;z)$], measuring the amount of information shared by any two variables without regard to the third; likewise we know how to estimate the amount of information in each variable *not* shared with another particular variable [namely, $H_y(x)$, $H_z(x)$, $H_x(y)$, $H_z(y)$, $H_x(z)$, and $H_y(z)$; see formulas (19) and (20)].

If the reader is not entirely clear on the reasoning which underlies the calculation of $\hat{T}(x;y)$ by formula (18),

$$\hat{T}(x;y) = \hat{H}(x) + \hat{H}(y) - \hat{H}(x,y)$$

he should review the relationships illustrated in Figure 5. By exactly the same reasoning, we may calculate the amount of information which any two variables (considered in combination, as if they were one) transmit to, or share with, a third:

$$\hat{T}(x,y;z) = \hat{H}(x,y) + \hat{H}(z) - \hat{H}(x,y,z) \qquad (34)$$

There are necessarily three T's of this sort: $T(y,z;x)$, the information which y and z jointly transmit to, or share with, x; $T(x,z;y)$, the information transmitted from x and z to y; and $T(x,y;z)$, the information transmitted from x and y to z. Corresponding to these three T's are three complementary functions, $H_{yz}(x)$, $H_{xz}(y)$, and $H_{xy}(z)$, which measure the amount of information *unique* to each variable. For example, $T(x,y;z)$ is that part of $H(z)$ which is shared with, or accounted for by, the other two variables, whereas $H_{xy}(z)$ is the remainder of $H(z)$, the component which is related to neither x nor y. Since $H(z)$ is thus composed of $T(x,y;z)$ and $H_{xy}(z)$, it follows that

$$\hat{H}_{xy}(z) = \hat{H}(z) - \hat{T}(x,y;z) \qquad (35)$$

and also, from formulas (34) and (35), that

$$\hat{H}_{xy}(z) = \hat{H}(x,y,z) - \hat{H}(x,y) \qquad (36)$$

as we might conclude by a more direct line of reasoning. Equations analogous to (34), (35), and (36) may of course be used to calculate the two similar $\hat{T}$'s and their complementary residuals.

The expression $T(x;y;z)$ refers to *all* the shared or nonunique information in the whole system:

$$\hat{T}(x;y;z) = \hat{H}(x,y,z) - \hat{H}_{yz}(x) - \hat{H}_{xz}(y) - \hat{H}_{xy}(z) \qquad (37)$$

or, more simply, going back to the rationale of formulas (18) and (34),

$$\hat{T}(x;y;z) = \hat{H}(x) + \hat{H}(y) + \hat{H}(z) - \hat{H}(x,y,z) \qquad (38)$$

A simple schematic representation of the relationships among these components (and others yet to be mentioned) would obviously aid our thinking at this point. The diagram in Figure 7 has considerable value as a summary of the relation-

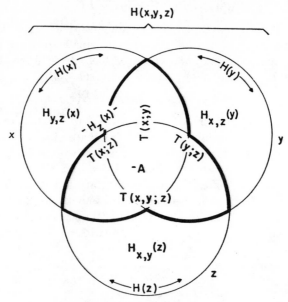

FIG. 7. First attempt to represent information sharing in the three-variable case.

ships discussed so far, though the reader should be given fair warning that a booby-trap lies ahead in this method of representation. The areas of three overlapping circles represent the information in our three variables x, y, and z: $H(x,y,z)$ is the total area occupied by the three circles; information shared by two variables [for example, $T(x;y)$] is represented by the area of overlap of two circles; information transmitted by two variables to a third [for example, $T(x,y;z)$] is represented by the overlap of two circles with a third, and so on. The labels written in are merely samples; the addition of many more would result in an intolerable clutter. There is no clear way to label $T(x;y;z)$, which is represented by the whole central area shaped like a flower with three petals. The reader should reconsider the formulas thus far derived, to see that they follow perfectly from the geometrical relationships of Figure 7.

Consider now the area marked $-A$, which represents (or appears to represent) any information shared by all three variables. It is evident from the geometry of Figure 7 that we may determine this area by subtracting the information jointly transmitted by any two variables to a third from the sum of their individual transmissions, thus:

$$[\hat{T}(x;z) + \hat{T}(y;z)] - \hat{T}(x,y;z)$$

or, equally well, by the subtraction

$$[\hat{T}(x;y) + \hat{T}(x;z) + \hat{T}(y,z)] - \hat{T}(x;y;z)$$

The joker is that typically (though not always) these subtractions yield a *negative* number! A negative value here at first seems quite absurd, not only because the idea of a negative area is repugnant, but also because it is difficult to see how all three variables could have less than no information in common.

Looking at the matter from another point of view, however, it is not strange that two variables considered in combination may give more information about a third than would the same two variables considered individually—indeed, this is the phenomenon of *interaction*, which is frequently encountered in analysis of variance. Suppose (as in one of the examples suggested earlier) that the three variables are stimuli, x, subjects, y, and responses, z. If different subjects apply different names to the stimuli, but do so consistently, we are likely to make a better prediction of a given subject's response to a given stimulus by considering how *he* usually responds to *this* stimulus then by combining a knowledge of his overall response tendencies (that is, pooled over all stimuli) with a knowledge of the responses which all subjects (considered as a group) tend to make to this stimulus. In other words, $\hat{T}$(stimulus, subject; response) is likely to be greater than $[\hat{T}$(subject; response) $+ \hat{T}$(stimulus; response)].

Interaction of this sort is an entirely different thing from the *overlap* of transmitted information from different sources, though the two are confounded computationally. A is defined as suggested earlier, but with the differences taken in the opposite direction; that is,

$$\hat{A}(x;y;z) = \hat{T}(x,y;z) - [\hat{T}(x;z) + \hat{T}(y;z)] \tag{39}$$

or,

$$\hat{A}(x;y;z) = \hat{T}(x;y;z) - [\hat{T}(x;y) + \hat{T}(x;z) + \hat{T}(y;z)] \tag{40}$$

So defined, A is a mixture of two components that cannot in general be measured separately: $A^{(-)}$ (transmission overlap) and $A^{(+)}$ (interaction). Thus $A = A^{(+)} - A^{(-)}$†. If interaction is the greater, as is usually the case, it will be positive.

The defect in Figure 7 is that it contains no representation of $A^{(+)}$, the interaction component. An attempt is made in Figure 8 to remedy this defect, with results that are only

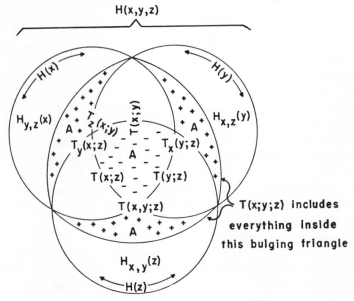

Fig. 8. Second attempt to represent information sharing in the three-variable case.

---

† This convenient way of expressing the composition of A is Quastler's [70].

moderately satisfactory. The reader must imagine that the three areas in which $A^{(+)}$ is shown are actually multiple appearances of the same area. Note that $T(x;y;z)$ and the three second-order transmission components such as $T(x,y;z)$ are now expanded to include $A^{(+)}$. As long as the reader is not misled by the multiple appearance of $A^{(+)}$, he will find the new diagram an isomorphic representation of all components, and relations among components, in the three-variable situation; he should at least identify all the terms of formulas (39) and (40) in the diagram, and see the geometrical relationships to which these equations correspond.

One further type of transmission function remains to be discussed; this is the information transmitted from one variable to another when the third is already known (or held constant, or "partialled out"). $T_z(x;y)$, for example [the other functions of this type are $T_x(y;z)$ and $T_y(x;z)$], is the information shared by x and y with z held constant.

There are several equivalent ways of calculating this measure; for example,

$$T_z(y;z) = T(x,y;z) - T(x;z) \tag{41}$$

or,
$$T_z(y;z) = H_z(y) + H_z(z) - H_z(y,z) \tag{42}$$

or,
$$T_z(y;z) = T(y;z) + A(x;y;z) \tag{43}$$

Since $A(x;y;z)$ may be either positive or negative, it is evident from formula (43) that $T_z(y;z)$ may be either greater or less than $T(y;z)$. Usually the measure of information shared by any two of the variables will be increased by holding the third constant, because interaction is likely to outweigh transmission overlap in usual experimental situations.

It should be borne in mind that the transmission function T is always a perfectly symmetrical measure of shared information, and that it need not imply any particular direction of causation: thus $T(y;x) = T(x;y)$, $T(x,y;z) = T(z;x,y)$, and $T_z(y;z) = T_z(z;y)$. A measure of relatedness which is *not* symmetrical, however, is the *coefficient of constraint*, D. The reader may recall, from the discussion of the Newman-Gerstman method in the previous chapter, that D is the proportion of the information in a specified variable which that variable shares with another. Since T necessarily involves two or more variables, it follows that for every T one might calculate at least two D's; for example,

$$D(x:y) = \frac{T(x;y)}{H(y)} \qquad (44)$$

$$D(y:x) = \frac{T(x;y)}{H(x)} \qquad (45)$$

D may also be applied to more complex relationships; for example,

$$D(x,y:z) = \frac{T(x,y;z)}{H(z)} \qquad (46)$$

$$D_x(y:z) = \frac{T_x(y;z)}{H_x(z)} \qquad (47)$$

$D(x:y)$ is the informational analogue of a simple correlation ratio; likewise $D(x,y:z)$ corresponds to multiple correlation, and $D_x(y:z)$ to partial correlation. The reader may have been impressed already by the similarity of the computational operations employed in multivariate informational analysis to the more familiar operations involved in analysis of variance. Some recent work by Garner and McGill [32] shows that this similarity is by no means superficial—that there is, in fact, a perfect one-to-one correspondence between the formal structure of variance-component or correlational analysis on one hand, and informational analysis on the other. This is not to imply that these two kinds of analysis are mathematically equivalent, as they are not;† the equivalence is instead on a logical or

---

† In certain special cases it is possible and legitimate to transform numerical results expressed in informational terms into terms of variance or correlation, and vice versa, but in general it must be considered that the two types of analysis involve qualitatively different units. Here is a striking example of the difference: let z be a set of random two-digit (decimal) numbers, x a set of one-digit numbers identical with the first digit of z, and y a set of one-digit numbers identical with the second digit of z. Now, x and y each share 3.32 bits of information with z, but $r_{xz} = .995$ and $r_{yz} = .10$; comparing the squares of these r's, we would say that x accounts for 99 times as much of the variance of z as does y.

structural level. The "metastatistics" which McGill and Garner seem to be developing may turn out to have great importance as a basic methodology for the study of interrelations among observed events.

Analyses involving four or more variables proceed according to the same general principles that have been outlined for the two- and three-dimensional cases. The four-dimensional analysis yields a simple A-term for each combination of three variables [for example, $A(w;x;z)$], an equal number of partial A's in which the fourth variable is held constant—for example,

$$A_w(x;y;z) = T_w(x;y;z) - [T_w(x;y) + T_w(x;z) + T_w(y;z)] \quad (48)$$

and one four-way A, which may be defined

$$A(w;x;y;z) = A_w(x;y;z) - A(x;y;z) \quad (49)$$

Further, it has been pointed out by Quastler [70] that a new *kind* of function, which he symbolizes B, makes its appearance for the first time in the four-dimensional case. The B associated with a particular variable measures the effect of that variable upon the total relatedness of the remainder of the system:

$$B(z:w;x;y) = T(z;w) + T(z;x) + T(z;y) - T(z;w,x,y)$$

$$= T(w;x;y) - T_z(w;x;y) \quad (50)$$

It is probable that the reader who has occasion to undertake an analysis involving four or more variables will find it necessary in any case to rely upon whatever insight into principles he may have gained from the consideration of simpler situations, and that further elaboration here would have little or no value. The preceding paragraph is included merely as a suggestive supplement to this necessary insight.

The three-variable analysis has been discussed in its most general and complex form, but in most applications it turns out to be much simpler. The simplification occurs whenever two of the three variables are independent and orthogonal. If x and y are two different stimulus variables, for example, they will ordinarily be kept independent of each other experimentally. The xy surface of the frequency table may therefore be ignored, in effect, since the experimental design will have provided that all the cells on this surface contain equal frequencies, and $T(x;y)$ will have the prearranged value of zero. But if $T(x;y) = 0$, there can be no *overlap* of transmission, $A^{(-)}$; therefore, $A = A^{(+)}$. It is only under this condition (namely, that all variables are orthogonal but one) that A may be interpreted as a pure *interaction* component.

An experimental design in which x is stimuli, y subjects, and z responses, enjoys the same advantages. McGill [51] did one such experiment in which the stimuli were 25 pointer positions on a vertical line. Eleven subjects attempted to identify these stimuli, when they were flashed on a screen, by pressing corresponding buttons. A total of 250 responses were obtained from each subject. Results of the analysis were as follows:

$$\hat{T}(\text{stimuli; responses}) = 2.40$$

$$\hat{T}(\text{subjects; responses}) = .12$$

$$\hat{A}(\text{stimuli; subjects; responses}) = .57$$

$$\hat{T}_{\text{subjects}}(\text{stimuli; responses}) = 2.40 + .57 = 2.97$$

$$\hat{T}_{\text{stimuli}}(\text{subjects; responses}) = .12 + .57 = .69.$$

In other words, a response from a given subject contained 2.97 bits of information about the stimulus (in comparison with the 2.40 bits about the stimulus contained in a response from an unknown subject); obversely, a response to a specified stimulus contained .69 bits about the subject making it, whereas a response to an unspecified stimulus conveyed virtually no information about the subject. The value of about three bits for the information transmitted by a given subject (equivalent to perfect identification of 8 alternative stimuli) is fairly typical of results which have been obtained with other stimulus dimensions, as we shall presently see.

Before we turn from statistics to experimental findings, however, there are two further matters, closely related to each other, which need to be considered. The first of these has to do with the *significance* of multivariate information transmission, the second with the *sampling bias* of information functions.

In the previous chapter we considered the relationship of $\hat{T}$ to χ^2:

$$\chi^2 = 1.3863n \times \hat{T}(x;y) \quad \text{(approximately)} \quad (51)$$

In other words, if $T(x;y)$ is really equal to zero (this is the null hypothesis which we test), then the sample estimate $\hat{T}(x;y)$, multiplied by 1.3863 times the number of observations, will be distributed approximately as χ^2. McGill [53], following the work of Miller and Madow [59], has investigated the applicability of this approximation to multivariate components. It appears, from his derivations, that the formula applies to *any* type of $\hat{T}$—including, for example $\hat{T}(x;y;z)$, $\hat{T}(x;y,z)$, and $\hat{T}_x(y;z)$—assuming always that the resulting χ^2 is evaluated according to the proper number of degrees of freedom. The significance of $\hat{A}$ may be determined in this way *only* in the case, referred to above, in which all the variables but one are orthogonal, and $\hat{A}$ is interpretable as a pure interaction component. In this case it may be transformed into a χ^2 by formula (51), precisely as if it were a $\hat{T}$. If $\hat{A}$ contains overlap as well as interaction, however, its significance may not be evaluated.

It is assumed that the reader has some rudimentary familiarity with the concept of "degrees of freedom" (df), as discussed in standard statistics texts, and with the calculation of degrees of freedom for contingency tables. This calculation is simplified, in the case of multivariate informational analysis, by the principle that *degrees of freedom combine in exactly the same way as the information components with which they are associated.* We need consider the frequency table only to determine the degrees of freedom of those values of $\hat{H}$ which are calculated directly from the table as in formulas (15) to (17) and (27) to (33). These degrees of freedom should be considered *negative* in sign, for reasons which will become clear as we proceed. In an X by Y table, it may be considered that df $= -(X - 1)$ for $H(x)$, $-(Y - 1)$ for $H(y)$, and $-(XY - 1)$ for $H(x,y)$. Now, $\hat{T}(x;y)$ is calculated by formula (18):

$$\hat{T}(x;y) = \hat{H}(x) + \hat{H}(y) - \hat{H}(x,y); \quad \text{therefore}$$

df of $\hat{T}(x;y) = -(X - 1) - (Y - 1) + (XY - 1) =$
$$XY - X - Y + 1 = (X - 1)(Y - 1),$$

which is a familiar expression for the degrees of freedom of χ^2 for an X by Y table. If x is an independent variable with a frequency distribution fixed by the experimenter, as in Table 4, we have an a priori or true value for $H(x)$, with zero degrees of freedom. In this case,

$$\hat{T}(x;y) = H(x) + \hat{H}(y) - \hat{H}(x,y), \quad \text{and}$$

df of $\hat{T}(x;y) = 0 - (Y - 1) + X(Y - 1) =$
$$XY - X - Y + 1 = (X - 1)(Y - 1)$$

again. Thus we see that it makes no difference to the degrees of freedom of $\hat{T}$ whether $\hat{H}(x)$ or $H(x)$ is used in calculating $\hat{T}$. For the remainder of this discussion, we shall assume that estimates such as $\hat{H}(x)$, $\hat{H}(y)$, etc., are always being used.

Degrees of freedom for the various transmission functions of the three-dimensional case may be calculated by the same principle. For example, the relations of formula (34), by which $\hat{T}(x,y;z)$ is calculated, apply as well to the degrees of freedom of the components involved:

$$\hat{T}(x,y;z) = \hat{H}(x,y) + \hat{H}(z) - \hat{H}(x,y,z), \quad \text{and}$$

df of $\hat{T}(x,y;z) = -(XY - 1) - (Z - 1) + (XYZ - 1)$
$$= XYZ - XY - Z + 1 = (XY - 1)(Z - 1)$$

In a similar manner formula (38) may be used to calculate that $\hat{T}(x;y;z)$ has df $= XYZ - X - Y - Z + 2$, and formula (41) to show that $\hat{T}_x(y;z)$ has df $= X(YZ - Y - Z + 1)$.

It should not be overlooked that χ^2 tests may also be applied to the various $\hat{H}$'s in the system. In the case of $\hat{H}$, however, the null hypothesis tested is not that $\hat{H} = 0$, but that $H_{max} - \hat{H} = 0$; in other words, that the frequencies from which H is calculated deviate only randomly from uniformity, and that the probabilities underlying these frequencies are all equal. The χ^2 for this test is given by

$$\chi^2 = 1.3863n(H_{max} - \hat{H}) \quad \text{(approximately)} \qquad (52)$$

Since H_{max} has df $= 0$, the df of $(H_{max} - \hat{H})$ is the same as that of $\hat{H}$, except for a change of sign; therefore the negative degrees of freedom attributed to $\hat{H}$ again become positive when associated with a χ^2.†

Implicit in the preceding discussion of χ^2 tests is the fact that both $\hat{H}$ and $\hat{T}$ are biased estimates of their respective true values, H and T. On the average, $\hat{H}$ will be less than H, and $\hat{T}$ will be greater than T. The meaning of this bias, in brief, is that sample values are not evenly distributed about the true value (as they are in the case of a distribution of sample means, for example), but instead tend to occur in one direction rather than the other. Consider some simple case in which the alternatives are actually equiprobable, and an $\hat{H}$ is calculated from a small sample of observed events. Unless these events are exactly evenly distributed over the possible categories (for example, unless a coin tossed 20 times lands *exactly* 10 times on heads, and 10 times on tails), the calculated value of $\hat{H}$ will be too low. Likewise, when two completely unrelated variables are represented in a contingency table of the sort we have been considering, unless all the cell proportions are exactly equal to the products of the marginal proportions (that is, in χ^2 jargon, unless O is exactly equal to E for every cell) a value of $\hat{T}$ greater than zero, the true value, will be obtained. With $T = 0$, sample values $\hat{T}$ will be distributed approximately as χ^2 (a one-tail distribution), as we have seen. This bias persists even when the true value of H is not maximal, or when the true value of T is not zero, though it necessarily diminishes at the opposite extreme as H approaches zero, or or as T approaches its maximum.

The work of Miller and Madow [59] provides an approximate correction for the bias of $\hat{H}$ and $\hat{T}$. If we still follow the con-

---

† Since the above discussion was written, several articles describing an "O minus E" method for the calculation of χ^2 values for interactions as well as main effects in the multivariate situation have appeared in psychological journals. See Sutcliffe, J. P. A general method of analysis of frequency data for multiple classification designs, *Psychol. Bull.*, 1957, 54, 134–137, for a clear description of the method and for references to mathematical sources. As we saw in the preceding section, however, it is actually easier to compute χ^2 values via informational components than by the "O minus E" procedure.

venient practice of considering the df of $\hat{H}$ to be negative, a single correction formula will serve for both functions:

$$H'(\text{or } T') = \hat{H}(\text{or } \hat{T}) - \frac{\text{df}}{1.3863n} \qquad (53)$$

in which H' or T' is the corrected value of $\hat{H}$ or $\hat{T}$. H' does not purport to be *equal* to the true value H, for sampling error remains; rather it is an *unbiased estimate* (or, one hopes, a less biased estimate) of H. The relationship of formula (53) to formulas (51) and (52) follows from the fact that the mean of a χ^2 distribution is equal to its degrees of freedom.

The correction should not be employed uncritically. Empirical evidence indicates that it is reasonably accurate, provided the following conditions are met: (1) The number of observations upon which the $\hat{H}$ or $\hat{T}$ is based should be fairly great: at the very least, n should be greater than df. This is not as easy a condition as it first appears; consider, for example, the degrees of freedom which $\hat{T}(x;y;z)$ may have. (2) The frequencies upon which the estimate is based should include few zero's, preferably none; otherwise the whole concept of degrees of freedom becomes fuzzy, and the value of df as usually calculated is likely to be too great by some indeterminate number (this is most striking in cases of near-perfect transmission). It should be added that these same restrictions apply to the approximation of χ^2 by formulas (51) and (52). If either or both of the above conditions are not met, the bias formula will overcorrect, and the χ^2 obtained will result in an underestimation of significance.[†]

Either the correlation coefficient, r, or the correlation ratio, η, uses fewer degrees of freedom than the corresponding $\hat{T}$, and therefore has greater stability. These measures of relatedness are accordingly preferable to $\hat{T}$ when stability is an im-

---

[†] The above discussion of sampling error is necessarily superficial, and merely suggests some of the serious problems which remain unsolved. The interested reader is referred especially to the papers on this subject by Miller, Rogers and Green, Augenstine, Blank and Quastler, and Attneave, in Quastler [70]. It appears that a satisfactory evaluation of the sampling error of information functions is going to require the use of Monte Carlo methods on high-speed computers to generate representative sampling distributions empirically.

portant issue, provided the data are such as to justify their use. (With merely nominal scaling on both of the related variables, neither of these measures may be applied; however, η may be applicable in the case of a nominal scale on one variable and an interval scale on the other, etc.) If one wishes to know how much information, in bits, the variables share, he may obtain an estimate of T from either r or η by a transformation discussed in Appendix I.

Experiments on Information Transmission

Having completed our excursion into statistical methodology, let us now consider some of the results which have been obtained by the use of informational analysis in absolute judgment situations. Hake and Garner [34] were the first experimenters to analyze data in this way. Their subjects had the task of identifying various positions of a pointer between two end markers (called 0 and 100) on a linear scale. The major experimental variable was the number of alternative positions—5, 10, 20, or 50—in which it was possible for the pointer to appear: for example, under the 5-alternative condition, only the positions 0, 20, 40, 60, 80, and 100 were allowed (0 and 100 were considered identical, since on an instrument scale the same marker serves as the end of one interpolation interval and the beginning of the next). Also varied was the restriction placed upon the subject's response: under one condition, he was told what the alternative positions would be, and responded by choosing one of them; under the other condition, he responded with any number from 0 to 100. The latter variable had little or no effect on the amount of information transmitted to the subject. With five alternative positions, about 2.30 bits-per-stimulus, out of a possible log 5 = 2.32, were transmitted to the subject; in other words, the subject lost practically none of the information presented. With 10, 20, or 50 alternatives, *transmitted information was approximately constant* at a value between 3.0 and 3.2 bits. This asymptotic value is roughly what would be obtained if nine alternatives were perfectly identified. The interesting conclusion of the study is that subjects can absolutely identify about nine points along a line, and that further increasing the number of alternatives does not increase the amount of information transmitted. The figures given above for transmitted information were obtained by calculating a value of $\hat{T}$ separately for each subject, and then averaging over all the subjects in a group. They are therefore identical with the values of $\hat{T}_{subjects}$(stimuli; responses) which would have been obtained if a trivariate analysis of the sort later developed by McGill had been done. In a very similar experiment previously mentioned, McGill calculated that 2.97 bits (corresponding to perfect identification of about eight alternatives) were conveyed by a pointer position to a subject. This figure is slightly lower than that of Hake and Garner, probably because McGill did not use end positions, whereas Hake and Garner did.

In 1952, Pollack [64] conducted a group of studies to determine the amount of information transmitted in absolute judgments of the pitch of pure tones. Under optimal conditions, $\hat{T}_{subjects}$(stimuli; responses) was found to be about 2.3 bits. Pooling subjects made little difference, however: T(stimuli; responses) was equal to 2.2 bits. This represents perfect identification of only about five alternatives. The contrast of this small number with the very great number of *just-noticeable-differences*, as defined by conventional psychophysical procedures, which have been estimated to exist along the pitch continuum, illustrates what is perhaps the most striking difference between the processes of discrimination and identification. Pollack verified the conclusion of Hake and Garner that increasing the number of alternatives beyond the maximum perfectly identified would not increase amount of information transmitted: he found little or no change in T when the number of alternative pitches was increased beyond 5. The most surprising of Pollack's findings, however, was that the *range* of frequencies covered by the alternative tones seemed to be almost negligible in importance. In a series of tests exploring eight alternative tones, the lowest was held constant at 100 cps, but the frequency of the highest was systematically varied from 500 to 8,000 cps, intermediate tones being equally spaced on a log scale. This variation in range—and in ratio between adjacent alternatives—of nearly 20 to 1 produced a variation of only about .2 bits, or roughly 10 percent, in the information transmitted by a tone! Likewise, it appeared to make little or no difference whether the tones were evenly spaced on the pitch scale or whether half were taken from the low end (100–250 cps) and half from the high end (2,000–8,000 cps). In short, the subjects' behavior suggested that they had about five pigeonholes into which they could sort tones by pitch, and that these same pigeonholes (but no more) could be freely rearranged along the pitch continuum to accommodate almost any distribution of stimuli.

Although subsequent experiments by Pollack and others have shown that transmitted information may be affected by the range and spacing of stimuli to a much greater degree than these early results suggested (see especially the recent review and discussion of Alluisi [2] in this connection), the opposite hypothesis that a separation of so-many j.n.d.'s is a necessary and sufficient condition for the differential identifiability of stimuli (as an uncomplicated theory in terms of "stimulus dispersions" or "stimulus-generalization gradients" is likely to assume) has in every case been found untenable. In one later study, Pollack [65] tried to increase the amount of transmitted information by first having subjects identify nine alternative tones, equally spaced along a logarithmic scale between 100 and 8,000 cps, and then adding two additional tones of 60 and 14,000 cps. Adding these two tones increased $\hat{T}$ by only .11 bits (from 2.29 to 2.40), less than one fourth the amount by which the tones might have increased $\hat{T}$ if they had been perfectly identified and had not disturbed the judgments of other tones. Actually, the added tones were themselves identified with great accuracy, but they caused the original nine to be confused more often. At the same time, Pollack investigated the effect of presenting an objective standard tone between the tones to be judged. When the sixth of the nine tones (ordered with respect to pitch) was used as a standard, transmission was increased appreciably—from 2.19 to 2.67 bits; a standard nearer either end of the frequency range was less effective.

A valuable study by Hartman [35] provides the only data

we have concerning the effects of prolonged practice on the information transmitted in absolute judgments. Four sets of nine pure tones differing in pitch were employed with as many groups; the spacing of tones was either 50, 100, 200, or 500 mels, depending on the group. Initially, the separation of the tones made relatively little difference: during the first week, values of $\hat{T}$ for the four groups were all within .3 bits (1.0–1.3) of one another. Over seven weeks of practice, during which incorrect judgments were corrected (except in one test session), the groups steadily diverged, until finally the tones 300 mels apart were conveying nearly a full bit more information (2.3 bits vs. 1.4 bits) than those only 50 mels apart. In terms of proportion of stimulus information transmitted—that is, $\hat{D}$(responses: stimuli)—the groups varied at first between about .32 and .43, and after practice between .44 and .73. Evidently the *opportunity for improvement* in precision of identification is limited by the separation or range of the stimuli. Even at the end of practice, however, tones equally different in pitch were not confused equally often by different groups: "Stimuli separated by equal pitch-distances are confused according to their position in the judgmental series. For example, tones 1, 5, and 9 are never confused by the 50-mel group, while the same frequencies (tones 4, 5, and 6) are confused almost one-third of the time by the 200-mel group." It should be mentioned that Hartman's transmission values are apparently in terms of $\hat{T}$(stimuli; responses), whereas those reported from Pollack are in terms of $\hat{T}_{subjects}$(stimuli; responses); this may partly explain why Hartman's initial values are somewhat lower than Pollack's.

The consistent finding that only about five different pitches can be absolutely identified (or six or seven, in the case of very good subjects) is in itself somewhat surprising. The information transmission of persons alleged to "have absolute pitch" has not been investigated, however. Moreover, neither Pollack nor Hartman used tones among which simple harmonic relationships obtained; one wonders whether the notes of a diatonic scale might not convey more information to musically experienced subjects, who might be expected to have some success in holding to the tonic of the scale as a subjective standard throughout an experimental session.†

Investigating absolute judgments of tones differing in loudness, Garner [29] has found that the maximum number of perfectly identifiable loudness levels is also about five. Using multivariate analysis techniques of the sort we have been considering, he studied the information contributed to responses, r, by the observer, o, and the preceding stimulus, p, as well as by the stimulus being judged, s. Number of stimulus categories varied from four to 20 for different groups, but always covered the same range (15–110 db). Garner found that the effects of o and p on r, as measured by $\hat{T}_s(o;r)$ and an approximation of $\hat{T}_s(o,p;r)$, were greater for tones of intermediate loudness than for extremes, and that these effects increased with number of stimulus categories. When data were pooled over o and p, the resulting values of $\hat{T}(s;r)$ were found to reach a maximum of about 2.1 bits with five stimulus categories, and thereafter to *decline*, reaching a value of about 1.6 bits with 20 categories. This apparent decline in transmission was clearly attributable to the increasing importance of o and p, however, since $\hat{T}(s,o;r)$ and an approximation of $\hat{T}(s,o,p;r)$ showed no such decline, and the latter even showed a slight increase, as the number of stimulus categories was increased from five to 20. The specific effect of p seemed to be one of assimilation rather than contrast: when the preceding stimulus was louder than the one being judged, the tendency was to overestimate, and vice versa.

Eriksen and Hake [24] have studied absolute judgments of squares varying in size. Under optimal conditions they obtained a $\hat{T}_{subjects}$(stimuli; responses) of about 2.2 bits, which is again equivalent to perfect identification of about five different stimulus values. Two different size-ranges were used: 2 to 42

---

† The day after I wrote the above paragraph, Dr. Miles Rogers told me about some unpublished work which he has done in the Harvard Psycho-Acoustic Laboratory on "absolute" judgments of pure musical tones. Ordinary subjects with good "relative pitch" gave judgments containing three to four bits of information, after practice, and one subject with "absolute pitch"—the concert-master of a symphony orchestra—was found to transmit 5.5 bits!

mm. sq. and 2 to 82 mm. sq. The superiority of the greater range was significant, but small, involving a difference in $\hat{T}$ of only about .2 bits. Number of stimulus categories and number of response categories were also varied in a factorial design; thus 5, 11, and 21 squares of different sizes were presented for judging, and 5, 11, and 21 alternative responses were available for expressing judgments, in the nine possible combinations of these conditions. $\hat{T}_{subjects}$(stimuli; responses) remained essentially constant over these variations, except when there were more stimulus categories than response categories—then transmission was poorer. The authors explain in considerable detail why this is the case, in terms of the distributions of responses to individual stimuli under the various conditions. Essential to their explanation is the fact (invariably found in absolute judgment situations) that the stimuli at either end of the range employed are identified much more consistently than those in between. Garner [29] also discusses this end-anchoring effect in his analysis of loudness judgments.

We have seen that the information conveyed by stimuli varying on a single dimension is likely to fall somewhere between 2 and 3 bits, and that increasing the number of alternative stimuli beyond the minimum mathematically necessary to transmit this limited amount of information results in little or no improvement of transmission (for a further discussion of this body of research see Miller [56].) Increasing the number of *dimensions* on which the stimuli may vary is quite a different matter. Klemmer and Frick [44] conducted an experiment in which a square containing one or more dots was briefly flashed on a screen before the subject, who attempted to reproduce the positions of the dots in a square provided on a response sheet. When the square contained only one dot, varying in location, 4.4 bits of information were transmitted. This value of $\hat{T}_{subjects}$ (stimuli; responses) is greater than any that is ever obtained (except in rare cases) for stimuli varying unidimensionally. A square containing one dot is obviously a two-dimensional display, since the dot may vary either vertically or horizontally, and two coordinates are required to specify its position. If the square is allowed to contain either one or two dots, it may be considered a four-dimensional display, since four coordinates are required to locate the two possible dots. With an eight-dimensional display—that is, a square containing one to four dots—Klemmer and Frick obtained a transmission of 7.8 bits. This value is probably too low, since each dot was allowed to take only three alternative positions on either of its dimensions (the value of 4.4 bits for one dot was obtained with six or more alternatives on either dimension).

In a later study, Pollack and Klemmer [67] used a display consisting of eight outline oblongs arranged in a horizontal line; one or more of these oblongs could be filled in to form "dots" on a given stimulus presentation. After a $\frac{1}{10}$-second exposure, the subject attempted to reproduce the dot pattern on a form. It may be considered that one number, or coordinate, is necessary to describe the position of each dot used in a pattern—at least up to the point at which dots outnumber unfilled oblongs. Thus one-dot patterns are unidimensional, patterns which may contain either one or two dots are in a sense two-dimensional, and so on. In Figure 9, amount of transmitted information, $\hat{T}_{subjects}(stimuli; responses)$, is plotted against the number of dimensions or "coordinality" of the display. As coordinates are added, $\hat{T}$ increases, but at a decreasing rate. Figure 9 shows that the increase in $\hat{T}$ is very nearly proportional to the increase in the logarithm of the number of coordinates; for example, doubling the number of coordinates increases $\hat{T}$ by about 1.7 bits, whether the doubling is from 1 to 2 or from 2 to 4. Plotted on the same graph are data from the Klemmer and Frick experiment in which dots in a square were presented; the agreement between the two experiments when their results are compared in this manner is remarkable.

Studies using auditory stimuli confirm the general principle that transmitted information increases with the number of stimulus aspects or dimensions. Pollack and Ficks [66] had subjects judge six aspects of an interrupted tone: frequency, loudness, rate of interruption, percentage time "on," total duration, and direction. With five steps on each dimension, total information transmitted per stimulus presentation ranged

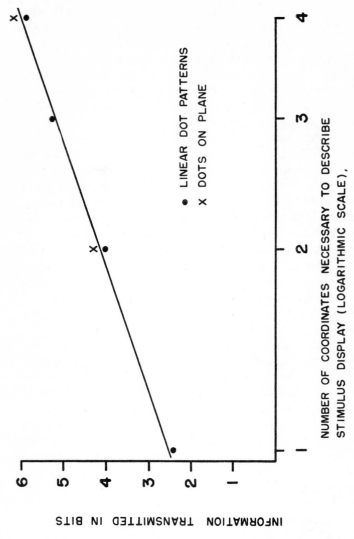

Fig. 9. Transmitted information as a function of the "coordinality" of the display. From Pollack and Klemmer [51], redrawn on a log scale.

from 6.2 bits for the poorest third of the subjects to 7.9 bits for the best third. These figures were obtained by calculating $\hat{T}_{subjects}$(stimuli, responses) separately for each dimension and summing over the six dimensions; since this procedure ignores interactions among the dimensions, the values reported are probably a little too low. In a simpler study, Pollack [65] was able to apply a full-scale multivariate analysis (involving the calculation of some 30 information components!) to judgments of tones varying in frequency and loudness. A total of 2.9 bits of transmitted information was obtained by calculating $\hat{T}$'s separately for the two dimensions and adding them together; this is only a little lower than the value of 3.1 bits calculated for transmission of the "pattern" of pitch and loudness—that is, taking interactions into account.

Thus the number of dimensions on which stimuli vary appears to be an extremely important psychological variable. For reasons other than psychological, MacKay [48, 49] proposed several years ago that two *kinds* of information—structural and metrical, or "logon content" and "metron content"— might profitably be distinguished in any body of data. The term "logon content" means essentially "dimensionality" or "degrees of freedom"; "metron content" is some function of the number of discriminable steps or categories on each dimension or logon. Such a distinction seems highly appropriate in the present context. In MacKay's formulation, different logons may represent scientific observations or measurements on independent physical variables, or they may represent multiple observations or measurements (each subject to some degree of error, which determines the metron content of the observation) on the same physical variable. An important experiment by Eriksen [23] is relevant to the latter case. He found a $\hat{T}$ of 4.1 for stimuli varying in size, brightness, and hue (compared with an average of 2.7 for these attributes employed separately) *even though the three attributes were perfectly correlated with one another*, so that any change in one always involved a concomitant change in each of the other two. It is evident, therefore, that amount of transmitted information is not directly dependent upon the physical dimensionality of the stimulus objects (that is, the number of independent ways in which the objects actually vary), but rather upon the dimensionality of the *observations* of the objects.

As we know from everyday experience, a tremendously large number of visual and auditory objects are constantly being identified with little or no error. Our high level of performance in identifying human faces, speech sounds, and other familiar stimuli is probably attributable to the fact that such objects differ from one another on a very large number of observational dimensions. Thus it is easy enough to employ an aggregate of perfectly identifiable stimuli in an absolute judgment experiment, but the results are uninteresting. More profitably, we may inquire *how rapidly* such stimuli transmit information to an observer—that is, we may shift our attention from bits-transmitted-per-stimulus-presentation (T) to bits-transmitted-per-second $(\dot{T})$.

A study by Sumby and Pollack [82] will serve to indicate some of the variables determining the rate at which individuals handle information. Subjects were required to transmit (that is, reproduce) verbal materials by writing, typing, and oral reading. The materials consisted of 12 different word-order approximations to English text (zero- to tenth-order, and text). These 50-word passages were constructed by a method described in the previous chapter, and the uncertainty-per-letter for each was measured by Shannon's guessing-game technique. The informational content of successive approximations followed a function very similar to that previously shown in Figure 4. In the case of all three reproduction tasks, the average time required to transmit a word likewise decreased as the order of approximation increased. The information transmitted, in bits-per-second, thus remained fairly constant for materials differing in redundancy. Although the authors do not report transmission rates as such, it appears that $\dot{T}$ reached a value of about 35 bits-per-second in the case of oral reading, which was the most rapid response medium. Sumby and Pollack further studied the effect on transmission time of selecting the words to be reproduced from a restricted vocabulary, with which the subjects were acquainted in advance. The size of the vocabulary was varied from 2 to 256 words; accordingly the informational content of a word varied from 1 to 8 bits. Although there was some increase in the average transmission time *per word* with increasing vocabulary size and information content, it was very slight—only about 10 percent over the whole range of conditions. The authors thus arrived at a very interesting pair of conclusions: that when *sequential* restrictions are varied within transmitted materials, the rate of information transmission remains nearly constant, but that when the *number of alternative units* is varied, transmission time per unit remains nearly constant, and rate of information transmission therefore increases with number of alternatives.

Evidence from other studies indicates that similar principles apply to immediate memory (and perhaps to long-range memory also). The reader will recall the Miller and Selfridge experiment [60], in which number of words correctly recalled increased with the order of approximation of the material to English text, amount of information recalled remaining approximately constant. On the other hand, Pollack [63] found, in a series of experiments on immediate recall, that the memory span for "message units" which are *not* sequentially restricted is practically constant, regardless of the number of alternatives from which the units are chosen. A subject was able to remember a sequence of about seven units, whether, for example, the units were random binary numbers (containing one bit each), decimal numbers (containing 3.3 bits each), or letters of the alphabet (containing 4.7 bits each). This constancy suggested to Smith and Miller [80] that it would be efficient for a subject to *recode* material into bigger "chunks." For example, he might recode a series of binary numbers into a third as many octal numbers, remembering the sequence "000" as "0," "001" as "1," "010" as "2," $\cdots$, and "111" as "7"; thus, if his memory span were for seven "chunks," he would be able to store 21 binary digits. Subjects who became adept at such recoding techniques did in fact show the predicted improvement, though not necessarily to the full degree suggested in the above example, since the recoding activity itself tended to interfere somewhat with memory. Miller [56] suggests that a very important part of the normal memory process may consist of recoding materials into verbal or conceptual "chunks" which contain progressively more and more information.

One reason why the same principles apply both to rate of transmission and to immediate memory may be that transmission (at least of the reproductive sort) *requires* the storage of information for brief intervals. A typist, for example, invariably "reads ahead" of the material being typed at the moment. Sumby and Pollack instructed subjects who reproduced the materials by writing to look at the material being copied no more often than they had to in order to maintain high speed and accuracy, and to return their eyes to the reproduction sheet after each look. The average number of glances per word necessary for transcribing materials of various statistical approximations to English is reported. Number of glances per word decreases over successive approximations much as does the informational content of the material and the time required to reproduce it. A glance is necessary for every three words of a zero-word-order passage, but only for every ten words of English text.

It is interesting that disjunctive reaction time, which involves no such storage process, seems to follow a somewhat different set of rules. A linear relationship has been found by Hick [40], and by Hyman [43], between reaction time and information per stimulus presentation, when information is varied by changing the number of stimulus alternatives between which a choice is to be made. What may be called choice time—that is, disjunctive reaction time minus simple reaction time—is very nearly *proportional* to bits per stimulus. The reaction time of Hyman's best subject was increased by about .127 seconds with each added bit. Moreover, Hyman found that approximately the same functional relationship between reaction time and stimulus information held regardless of *how* the latter was varied—whether by varying number of equiprobable alternatives, relative frequency of alternatives, or sequential dependencies between stimuli. The *degree* of relationship (as measured by correlation coefficients) was not entirely constant for the three forms of variation, being lowest in the case of variations in sequential dependencies.

An experiment by Klemmer and Muller [45] further supports the principle that rate of *continuous* information transmission increases with number of alternative stimuli. A line of one to five light bulbs was displayed to the subject; a response button corresponding to each light bulb was placed under one of his fingers. However many bulbs were present in a given test, the various possible patterns of lights (4 with 2 bulbs, 8 with 3 bulbs, etc.) were presented in random sequence, and the subject attempted to reproduce each pattern by pressing the appropriate buttons. In some tests, presentation rate was controlled by the experimenter; in others, the subject's response triggered off the next stimulus. The rate of information transmission attained by subjects highly practiced in this task was found to be very nearly proportional to the bits-per-stimulus-pattern—that is, to the number of light bulbs. A subject tended spontaneously to adopt his optimal speed under conditions of self-pacing; if this rate of presentation was exceeded in the forced-pacing condition, errors quickly appeared and rate of transmitted information declined.

Quastler and Wulff [71] have investigated the peak transmission rates attained in a variety of well-practiced sequential tasks. In one experiment they estimated the rate of information transmission by expert pianists. Since music is ordinarily highly redundant, random sequences of notes were prepared. The range of alternative notes from which these were chosen was varied from three (1.6 bits per note) to 65 (6.0 bits per note). An estimated $\dot{T}$ of about 22 bits per second was the maximum obtained. An optimal range of alternatives seemed to be anywhere between 15 and 37 notes; with as many as 65 alternatives, transmission rate declined. The basis for this decline may have been largely on the motor side, since so great a range of equiprobable notes made for large "jumps" on the keyboard between successive keys. Likewise, the nature of musical notation is such that some difficulty in *identifying* notes may arise when intervals are very large. A similar experiment was conducted to determine the maximum transmission rate attained in typing. Sequences of 100 symbols were chosen randomly from classes of 4, 8, 16, or 32 alternatives. The rate of transmission increased steadily with number of alternative symbols (despite the fact that the 4- and 8-alternative passages were confined to the "home" keys of the typewriter) from an estimated value of 5 bits-per-second with four keys to a maximum of about 15 bits-per-second with 34 keys. This maximum is still considerably below the 22 bits-per-second obtained for piano playing. From a survey of several studies, Quastler and Wulff estimate that the maximum rate of impromptu speaking is about 26 bits-per-second, and the mean rate about 18. It is estimated that in silent reading the $\dot{T}$ may be as high as 44.

Most ingenious of all is the informational analysis which Quastler and Wulff make of the performance of a famous "lightning calculator," J. M. F. Dase. Working from a set of plausible assumptions concerning the specific operations employed by such an individual in mental multiplication, they estimate that Dase's maximum rate of information processing (in calculating the product of two 8-digit numbers in 54 seconds) was about 24 bits-per-second—roughly the same as that of an expert pianist! Quastler and Wulff found at least one person in their laboratory who could do mental arithmetic at this rate, but only for very short periods of time. "Thus," they conclude, "what makes a 'lightning' calculator is the ability to carry on in orderly fashion for very long stretches, plus a memory for figures which is several times the ordinary span of 6.6 digits, but not a particularly high rate of handling information. One point of particular interest is that the calculations are performed with little or no conscious control. Thus we have one situation where the famed rapidity of subconscious thinking can be tested; it turns out to be not too impressive."

CHAPTER 4

A New Approach to Some Old Problems

Information theory is not psychological theory. A technique like the Garner-Hake-McGill method of informational analysis is as completely neutral with respect to psychological schools and controversies as is analysis of variance or χ^2. Yet it would be quite unrealistic to deny that certain broad concepts of information theory, which have little or nothing to do with specific statistical techniques, are also having their effect on psychological thinking. For an example: the work of Hovland and Weiss [41, 42] on the relative contribution of positive and negative instances to concept formation takes its "approach" from information theory, though the authors are not concerned with information in terms of bits.

It is also undeniable that the concepts of information theory are peculiarly compatible with certain points of view in psychology—particularly with the probabilistic functionalism of Brunswik [17, 18], and with statistical theories of behavior like those of Estes [25, 26] and Bush and Mosteller [19, 20]. Binder [15] has presented a statistical model for the process of visual recognition which makes explicit use of informational concepts and measures. Again, it will be evident to any reader who has given consideration to hypothetical nerve nets of the Pitts-McCulloch type [50] that such nets may be described fairly easily, and quite exhaustively, in informational terms. Rapoport's [72] application of information networks to a theory of vision is a good illustration of this point.

One of the great fascinations of information theory for the psychologist, as Miller [55] has emphasized, is that it offers a methodology for quantifying *organization*, or *patterning*. Gestalt psychologists have been vigorously attacked in the past for assigning a major importance to these concepts, on the grounds that they are subjective, unquantifiable, perhaps even a trifle ghostly. Such arguments no longer have much weight, since organization is demonstrably measurable in informational terms: roughly speaking, organization and redundancy are the same. On the other hand, gestalt psychologists must now be prepared to see their most cherished principles subjected to experimental tests which have hitherto been impossible, and perhaps modified as a result.

Hochberg and McAlister [39] and I [4] independently arrived at the view that "figural goodness" and related gestalt concepts might be reformulated in informational terms and thus rendered more amenable to quantitative treatment (other psychologists, notably Dr. Paul M. Fitts and his associates [27, 85], were simultaneously thinking along the same lines). I used the guessing-game technique of Shannon to demonstrate that principles of perceptual grouping such as *similarity* and *good continuation* refer to various types of redundancy which may exist within a static visual field, enabling an observer to "predict" portions of the field with great accuracy from a knowledge of other portions. I suggested that perception might be conceived as a set of preliminary "data-reduction" operations, whereby sensory information is described, or encoded, in a form more economical than that in which it impinges on the receptors. Hochberg and McAlister discussed the gestalt organizational principles in somewhat similar terms, giving particular attention to cases of ambiguous organization.

They proceeded to test the hypothesis "that the probability of a given perceptual response to a stimulus is an inverse function of the amount of information required to define that pattern." The Kopferman "cubes," a set of figures which may be perceived either bidimensionally or tridimensionally, were employed as stimuli. Results were as predicted: the smaller the number of lines, angles, and intersections in a figure, the greater was the proportion of bidimensional responses to it (tridimensional complexity was the same for all figures, since they were all aspects of a cube). Hochberg and Levitt [38] later confirmed these results using a wider range of stimuli.

It may be demonstrated (for instance, by the guessing-game technique) that angles and intersections are regions of high informational content in the visual field. Hochberg and his associates have contented themselves with merely counting these surprisal peaks to obtain a measure crudely proportional to the information in a figure, refraining (wisely, I think) from any attempt to use the Shannon-Wiener measure. A visual stimulus array may not be said to contain any determinate number of *bits* of information until its grain—the size of its smallest elements—is specified. Specifying the effective grain of a display which is not artificially constructed, however, involves problems which, though not necessarily insoluble, are extraordinarily troublesome. What we need is a measure of the information in a visual field that is not dependent upon grain. It appears that the "logon content" [48] or "coordinality" [67] of the stimulus may come very close to meeting this need. Within broad limits, coordinality is independent of grain; however, it will almost certainly be proportional to information-in-bits, to a first approximation, once any particular grain is specified. By assuming certain basic reduction principles of the sort which I list in the article cited earlier, one may hope to arrive at a reasonable estimate of the minimum number of numbers, or coordinates, necessary to describe a display. We should constantly bear in mind, however, that the subject need not perceive objects in accordance with the experimenter's descriptive system: indeed, it is from just these discrepancies that we acquire new knowledge about the nature of perceptual processes. One such set of discrepancies gives rise to the important distinction between "bits" and "chunks." Again, an experiment of my own [7] has shown that the *judged* complexity of shapes may or may not vary with their informational content, depending upon the way in which information is varied. Judged complexity increases logarithmically with the number of sides in a polygon, but the grain of the matrix in which the polygon is constructed makes no difference. This result would suggest that "logon content," rather than "metron content," determines judged complexity; however, the introduction of curvature in the shapes increases logon content but has no effect on complexity judgments.

A further concept which offers attractive but unexplored possibilities for the description of stimuli is Rashevsky's measure of *topological information content* [73, 83, 84]. Given any group of points which are connected in certain ways, one may sort the points into classes according to their topological properties, points within a class being topologically indistinguishable from one another. These classes may be considered analogous to symbols or alternative events in a communications system. The familiar measure $\sum p \log \dfrac{1}{p}$ is applied by summing over all these topologically different classes, with p interpreted as the proportion of points in each class.

Stimuli for experimental use may readily be constructed to contain any desired number of bits, of course, since the experimenter is free to choose any grain that suits his purposes, and to make the grain as well as the dimensions of variability known to his subjects if he wishes. (See Attneave and Arnoult [8] for a general discussion of quantitative methods for shape and pattern construction.) The materials for several recent studies of pattern identification have been quantified in this way. Weinstein and Fitts [85] used histogramlike patterns varying in complexity (that is, informational content) in a task similar to card sorting, and found that identification time increased with complexity (the stimuli always contained enough information to allow unequivocal sorting). Bricker [16] obtained similar results from a paired-associates learning experiment in which "stimulus redundancy"† was varied by adding elements (dots) to the minimum number of elements necessary to identify each stimulus. Increasing complexity beyond the necessary minimum retarded learning, making identification more difficult, except under a "noisy" condition in which incomplete patterns were presented. These results are somewhat surprising: one might expect that stimuli would be easier to identify the more alternative cues for identification they possessed, but this is clearly not the case. Whether or not simple stimuli remain easier to identify than complex ones after intensive overlearning is a question that deserves further investigation.

"Good" figures are supposed to be better remembered than "poor" ones. But if figural goodness is equivalent to redundancy, we are led to suspect that "good" figures may be easier for the reason that they contain less information to be remembered. Recently I tested this hypothesis in a trio of experiments [5] involving immediate reproduction, delayed reproduction (after repeated exposures), and identification, respectively, of patterns of dots in rectangular matrices. For some groups, the patterns were symmetrical: of all the possible forms of redundancy, symmetry is the easiest to quantify in an objective and unequivocal way. The design of all three experiments was such as to permit comparison between memory for symmetrical patterns and memory for (1) random patterns with the same informational content (and hence fewer cells), and (2) random patterns occupying the same number of cells (and hence containing more information). The hypothesis tested was somewhat more than confirmed: in the two reproduction experiments, symmetrical patterns were recalled significantly *less* accurately than asymmetrical patterns of equivalent

_____

† Bricker's usage of "redundancy" is somewhat different from mine [4, 5]. I consider "redundant" the information which various stimulus components share with one another; whereas for Bricker, information in excess of that necessary for the determination of certain specified naming or categorizing responses is "redundant." These two meanings of "redundancy" are closely related to each other, but the relationship is not a simple one.

informational content! In the case of immediate reproduction, they were only a little easier to recall than asymmetrical patterns containing the same number of elements, but this difference was much greater in the case of delayed reproduction, suggesting that appreciable time is required for the economical encoding, or organizing, of redundant patterns. In the identification experiment, symmetrical patterns were approximately equal in difficulty to random patterns containing the same information. As in the studies of Bricker and others, random patterns were harder to identify the greater their informational content.

These results with redundant visual patterns are similar, with one interesting exception, to results which Aborn and Rubenstein [1, 74] earlier obtained with verbal materials. They required subjects to learn sequences of nonsense syllables into which certain sequential dependencies, following principles fairly easy to learn, were introduced. Subjects recalled *less information* (but a greater total amount of material) from highly "organized" or redundant lists than from lists with less "organization" or redundancy. Rubenstein and Aborn thought that amount of information recalled might be more nearly constant if subjects were given more study time; when study time was actually varied, however, the opposite result was obtained: the more time subjects had to study the lists, the greater was the disparity between lists of high and low organization. This result is extremely puzzling; it is in disagreement not only with the authors' expectation, but also, apparently, with the difference which I found between "immediate reproduction" (in which patterns were exposed only once) and "delayed reproduction" (in which patterns were exposed repeatedly and longer.†

The importance of perceptual and conceptual *schemata* has been recognized by many psychologists, including Bartlett [9], Woodworth [87, p. 74, etc.], and Hebb [36]. Both Hochberg and I [37, 4, 6] have pointed out the relevance of schemata to

---

† Cf. also the memory studies of Miller and Selfridge [60], Marks and Jack [47], and Pollack [63], which have been cited previously.

economical encoding (Hochberg in a discussion of social stereo-
types), but the most detailed and interesting presentation of
this idea is that of Oldfield [62]. He considers, as a simplified
model of the organism, a computer which must store sequences
of binary numbers. Patterns of numbers which recur frequently
(analogous to patterns of stimulus elements arising from
familiar objects in the organism's environment) may be recoded
into briefer form. Any such recurrent combination is potentially
a schema (corresponding, at the simplest level, to an object or
a class of objects); with experience, the computer builds up a
set of abbreviated code symbols for many such schemata.
When the computer receives a sequence of numbers *almost*
coincident with one of its schemata, the most economical storage
procedure will consist of recording (1) the short code symbol
for the schema, and (2) a record of deviations from the schema
(that is, new information) in the present sequence. To give a
common-sense example of the psychological analogue: when
one is first introduced to a new acquaintance, it is unnecessary
to memorize the separate facts that he has ten fingers, that
his head is located above his body, that his ears are on opposite
sides of his head, etc., etc., since these are all parts of the
familiar schema *man*; what is important is to remember the
characteristics distinguishing *this* man from all others. Oldfield
further suggests that the process of encoding may proceed
through several successive stages, the recoded form of the
input being further recoded, and so on, forming a hierarchy of
schemata (much like the hierarchy of Hebb's theory). He
shows that certain *formal similarities* between sequences will
be reduced to identities only after several such stages of recoding.
Finally, he supposes that the computer might continually
search through material already stored for regularities which
would permit more economical recoding and restorage. Such
a process would resemble—or perhaps constitute—inductive
reasoning.

The view that a basic function of psychoneural activity is
the economical encoding of experience may be elaborated in
many ways. It has extraordinary generality, applying to the
most complex scientific thinking as well as to the basic processes

of perception and memory. We know, of course, that organisms rarely if ever encode their experience with *optimal* economy, but an interesting way of studying their processes is by determining how, and to what degree, they fall short of this ideal.

A number of the ideas discussed in this section have been employed in a somewhat different way by Berlyne [11, 12, 13, 14], who is seriously attempting to achieve a theoretical integration of such variables as emotional disturbance, reaction time, drive, curiosity, stimulus complexity, and reward within a stimulus-response framework. He suggests that "conflict," or competition among responses, may underlie all these phenomena, and that either the uncertainty function of information theory or some similar measure may be used to quantify degree of conflict [13]. In a series of interesting experiments on curiosity and orienting responses, Berlyne has found a consistent relationship between the amount of information in a stimulus object and the degree of curiosity or attention which it evokes, whether amount of information is varied by manipulating number of stimulus elements, regularity (redundancy) of elements, or degree of deviation from familiar schemata.

Although the techniques of information theory are useful in the study of the organism's information-handling processes, other techniques may often be more useful and more appropriate. That aspect of information measures which gives them so wide a range of application also limits their usefulness in any specific area. Having determined that a sequence of symbols is redundant, for example, we often wish to know what kind of redundancy is involved, and what kind of encoding would remove it; having found that two variables are related by a sizable value of T, we are curious to know *how* they are related. Information measures do not give us the answers to these questions. The value of the concepts of information theory in leading us into new areas of investigation is not lessened, however, if in the pursuit of these investigations we find it possible to abandon information measures in favor of others more informative.

References

1. Aborn, M. and Rubenstein, H. Information theory and immediate recall. *J. exp. Psychol.*, 1952, 44, 260–266.
2. Alluisi, E. A. Conditions affecting the amount of information in absolute judgments. *Psychol. Rev.*, 1957, 64, 97–103.
3. Attneave, F. Psychological probability as a function of experienced frequency. *J. exp. Psychol.*, 1953, 46, 81–86.
4. Attneave, F. Some informational aspects of visual perception. *Psychol. Rev.*, 1954, 61, 183–193.
5. Attneave, F. Symmetry, information, and memory for patterns. *Amer. J. Psychol.*, 1955, 68, 209–222.
6. Attneave, F. Transfer of experience with a class-schema to identification-learning of patterns and shapes. *J. exp. Psychol.*, 1957, 54, 81–88.
7. Attneave, F. Physical determinants of the judged complexity of shapes. *J. exp. Psychol.*, 1957, 53, 221–227.
8. Attneave, F. and Arnoult, M. D. The quantitative study of shape and pattern perception. *Psychol. Bull.*, 1956, 53, 452–471.
9. Bartlett, F. C. *Remembering*. London: Cambridge Univ. Press, 1932.
10. Bendig, A. W. Twenty questions: an informational analysis. *J. exp. Psychol.*, 1953, 46, 345–348.
11. Berlyne, D. E. Conflict and choice time. *Brit. J. Psychol.*, 1957, 48, 106–118.
12. Berlyne, D. E. Conflict and information-theory variables as determinants of human perceptual curiosity. *J. exp. Psychol.*, 1957, 399–404.
13. Berlyne, D. E. Uncertainty and conflict: a point of contact between information-theory and behavior-theory concepts. *Psychol. Rev.*, 1957, 64, 329–339.
14. Berlyne, D. E. The influence of complexity and novelty in visual figures on orienting responses. *J. exp. Psychol.*, 1958, 55, 289–296.
15. Binder, A. A statistical model for the process of visual recognition. *Psychol. Rev.*, 1955, 62, 119–129.
16. Bricker, P. D. The identification of redundant stimulus patterns. *J. exp. Psychol.*, 1955, 49, 73–81.

17. Brunswik, E. *Systematic and representative design of psychological experiments: with results in physical and social perception.* Berkeley: Univ. of California Press, 1947.
18. Brunswik, E. *The conceptual framework of psychology.* Chicago: Univ. of Chicago Press, 1952.
19. Bush, R. R. and Mosteller, F. A mathematical model for simple learning. *Psychol. Rev.,* 1951, 58, 313–323.
20. Bush, R. R. and Mosteller, F. A model for stimulus generalization and discrimination. *Psychol. Rev.,* 1951, 58, 412–423.
21. Coupling, J. J. Chance remarks. *Astounding Science Fiction,* 1948, 44, 104–111.
22. Culbertson, J. T. *Consciousness and behavior.* Dubuque, Iowa: Brown, 1950.
23. Eriksen, C. W. Multidimensional stimulus differences and accuracy of discrimination. USAF: *WADC Technical Report,* 54–165, 1954.
24. Eriksen, C. W. and Hake, H. W. Absolute judgments as a function of the stimulus range and the number of stimulus and response categories. USAF: *WADC Technical Report,* 54–162, April 1954.
25. Estes, W. K. Toward a statistical theory of learning. *Psychol. Rev.,* 1950, 57, 94–104.
26. Estes, W. K. and Burke, C. J. A theory of stimulus variability in learning. *Psychol. Rev.,* 1953, 60, 276–286.
27. Fitts, P. M., Weinstein, M., Rappaport, M., Anderson, N., and Leonard, A. J. Stimulus correlates of visual pattern recognition. *J. exp. Psychol.,* 1956, 51, 1–11.
28. Frick, F. C. and Miller, G. A. A statistical description of operant conditioning. *Amer. J. Psychol.,* 1951, 64, 20–36.
29. Garner, W. R. An informational analysis of absolute judgments of loudness. *J. exp. Psychol.,* 1953, 46, 373–380.
30. Garner, W. R. Symmetric uncertainty analysis and its implications for psychology. *Psychol. Rev.,* 1958, 65, 183–196.
31. Garner, W. R. and Hake, H. W. The amount of information in absolute judgments. *Psychol. Rev.,* 1951, 58, 446–459.
32. Garner, W. R. and McGill, W. J. Relation between uncertainty, variance, and correlation analyses. *Psychometrika,* 1956, 21, 219–228.
33. Guilford, J. P. *Psychometric methods.* New York: McGraw-Hill, 1936.
34. Hake, H. W. and Garner, W. R. The effect of presenting various numbers of discrete steps on scale reading accuracy. *J. exp. Psychol.,* 1951, 42, 358–366.
35. Hartman, E. B. The influence of practice and pitch-distance between tones on the absolute identification of pitch. *Amer. J. Psychol.,* 1954, 67, 1–14.
36. Hebb, D. O. *Organization of behavior.* New York: Wiley, 1949.

37. Hochberg, J. E. Psychophysics and stereotypy in social perception. In *Emergent problems in social psychology*. In press.
38. Hochberg, J. E. and Levitt, D. Figural "goodness" and information. Manuscript.
39. Hochberg, J. E. and McAlister, E. A quantitative approach to figural "goodness." *J. exp. Psychol.*, 1953, 46, 361–364.
40. Hick, W. E. On the rate of gain of information. *Quart. J. exp. Psychol.*, 1952, 4, 11–26.
41. Hovland, C. I. A "communication analysis" of concept learning. *Psychol. Rev.*, 1952, 59, 461–472.
42. Hovland, C. I. and Weiss, W. Transmission of information concerning concepts through positive and negative instances. *J. exp. Psychol.*, 1953, 45, 175–182.
43. Hyman, R. Stimulus information as a determinant of reaction time. *J. exp. Psychol.*, 1953, 45, 188–196.
44. Klemmer, E. T. and Frick, F. C. Assimilation of information from dot and matrix patterns. *J. exp. Psychol.*, 1953, 45, 15–19.
45. Klemmer, E. T. and Muller, P. F. The rate of handling information. Key pressing responses to light patterns. *HFORL Memo Report*, No. 34, March 1953.
46. Leary, R. W., Harlow, H. F., Settlage, P. H., and Greenwood, D. D. Performance on double-alternation problems by normal and brain-injured monkeys. *J. comp. physiol. Psychol.*, 1952, 45, 576–584.
47. Marks, M. R. and Jack, O. Verbal context and memory span for meaningful material. *Amer. J. Psychol.*, 1952, 65, 298–300.
48. MacKay, D. M. Quantal aspects of scientific information. *Phil. Mag.*, 1950, 41, 289–311.
49. MacKay, D. M. The nomenclature of information theory. In H. von Foerster (ed.), *(Transactions of the eighth conference on) Cybernetics; circular causal and feedback mechanisms in biological and social systems*. New York: Josiah Macy, Jr., Foundation, 1952.
50. McCulloch, W. S. and Pitts, W. A logical calculus of the ideas immanent in nervous activity. *Bull. Math. Biophys.*, 1943, 5, 115–133.
51. McGill, W. J. The relation between error variance and information transmitted in a simple pointing task. Unpublished note.
52. McGill, W. J. Multivariate transmission of information and its relation to analysis of variance. *HFORL Report*, No. 32.
53. McGill, W. J. Multivariate information transmission. *Psychometrika*, 1954, 19, 97–116.
54. McNemar, Q. *Psychological statistics*. New York: Wiley, 1949.
55. Miller, G. A. What is information measurement? *Amer. Psychologist*, 1953, 8, 3–11.
56. Miller, G. A. The magical number seven, plus or minus two: some

limits on our capacity for processing information. *Psychol. Rev.*, 1956, 63, 81–97.

57. Miller, G. A. and Frick, F. C. Statistical behavioristics and sequences of responses. *Psychol. Rev.*, 1949, 56, 311–324.

58. Miller, G. A., Heise, G. A., and Lichten, W. The intelligibility of speech as a function of the context of the test materials. *J. exp. Psychol.*, 1951, 41, 329–335.

59. Miller, G. A. and Madow, W. G. On the maximum likelihood estimate of the Shannon-Wiener measure of information. Air Force Cambridge Research Center: *Technical Report*, 54–75, August 1954.

60. Miller, G. A. and Selfridge, J. A. Verbal context and the recall of meaningful material. *Amer. J. Psychol.*, 1950, 63, 176–185.

61. Newman, E. B. and Gerstman, L. S. A new method for analyzing printed English. *J. exp. Psychol.*, 1952, 44, 114–125.

62. Oldfield, R. C. Memory mechanisms and the theory of schemata. *British J. Psychol.*, 1954, 45, 14–23.

63. Pollack, I. The assimilation of sequentially-encoded information. *HFORL Memo Report*, No. 25, September 1952, and *HFORL Report*, TR-54-5, January 1954.

64. Pollack, I. The information of elementary auditory displays. *J. Acoust. Soc. Am.*, 1952, 24, 745–749.

65. Pollack, I. The information of elementary auditory displays, II. *J. Acoust. Soc. Am.*, 1953, 25, 765–769.

66. Pollack, I. and Ficks, L. Information of multidimensional auditory displays. *J. Acoust. Soc. Am.*, 1954, 26, 155–158.

67. Pollack, I. and Klemmer, E. T. The assimilation of visual information from linear dot patterns. Air Force Cambridge Research Center: *Technical Report*, 54–16, July 1954.

68. Quastler, H. (ed.) *Essays on the use of information theory in biology.* Urbana: Univ. of Illinois Press, 1953.

69. Quastler, H. and Blank, A. A. Notes on the estimation of information measures. University of Illinois, *Control Systems Lab. Report*, No. r-56, May 1954.

70. Quastler, H. (ed.) *Information theory in psychology: problems and methods.* Proceedings of the conference on the Estimation of Information Flow, Monticello, Illinois, July 5–9, 1954, and related papers. Glencoe, Illinois: Free Press, 1955.

71. Quastler, H. and Wulff, V. J. Human performance in information transmission. Part one: simple sequential routinized tasks. Manuscript.

72. Rapoport, A. Application of information networks to a theory of vision. *Bull. Math. Biophys.*, 1955, 17, 15–33.

73. Rashevsky, N. Life, information theory, and topology. *Bull. Math. Biophys.*, 1955, 17, 229–235.

74. Rubenstein, H. and Aborn, M. Immediate recall as a function of

degree of organization and length of study period. *J. exp. Psychol.*, 1954, 48, 146–152.

75. Samson, E. W. *Fundamental natural concepts of information theory.* Air Force Cambridge Research Station: Report E5079, 1951.

76. Senders, V. L. Further analysis of response sequences in the setting of a psychophysical experiment. *Amer. J. Psychol.*, 1953, 66, 215–228.

77. Senders, V. L. and Sowards, A. Analysis of response sequences in the setting of a psychophysical experiment. *Amer. J. Psychol.*, 1952, 65, 358–374.

78. Shannon, C. E. Prediction and entropy of printed English. *Bell Syst. tech. J.*, 1951, 30, 50–64.

79. Shannon, C. E. and Weaver, W. *The mathematical theory of communication.* Urbana: Univ. of Illinois Press, 1949.

80. Smith, S. L. and Miller, G. A. The effects of coding procedures on learning and memory. Quarterly progress report of Research Laboratory of Electronics, MIT, to Air Force Human Resources Research Laboratories. December 1952, 7–10.

81. Stevens, S. S. Measurement, psychophysics, and utility. Paper presented in Symposium on Measurement at December 1956 meeting of AAAS.

82. Sumby, W. H. and Pollack, I. Short-time processing of information. *HFORL Report*, TR-54-6, January 1954.

83. Trucco, E. A note on the information content of graphs. *Bull. Math. Biophys.*, 1956, 18, 129–135.

84. Trucco, E. On the information content of graphs: compound symbols; different states for each point. *Bull. Math. Biophys.*, 1956, 18, 237–253.

85. Weinstein, M. and Fitts, P. M. A quantitative study of the role of stimulus complexity in visual pattern discrimination. *Amer. Psychologist*, 1954, 9, 490. (abstract)

86. Wiener, N. *Cybernetics.* New York: Wiley, 1948.

87. Woodworth, R. S. *Experimental psychology.* New York: Holt, 1938.

Appendix I

The Calculation of Information Measures
from Variance Statistics

The correlation coefficient, r, the correlation ratio, η (eta), and the transmission function, T, are alike in that all three are measures of relatedness. T is the most general of the three, since it may be calculated for any transmission matrix of the sort shown in Table 3 (p. 45), whether the variables are ordered —that is, whether adjacent categories represent successive steps on a continuum—or not. When the variables are ordered, but not related in a linear manner, either T or η may be calculated, and when a linear relationship holds, either T, η, or r may be. In the last case, η and r will be equal, or very nearly so: the square of either may be interpreted as the proportion of the variance of y which is predicted, or accounted for, by x. But how is T related to r and η? This relationship has a practical importance as well as a theoretical interest. The stability of a sample value of r (or of η, though to a lesser degree) is much greater than that of $\hat{T}$, because $\hat{T}$ involves many more degrees of freedom; therefore, if we had a matrix containing many cells and relatively few observations, and a linear relationship held between the variables, an estimate of T calculated from r might be considerably more accurate than one calculated by the use of the Shannon-Wiener measure.

Now, it may be shown (see Shannon [79] pp. 54–56) that the uncertainty associated with a *normal distribution* is

$$H = \log \sqrt{2\pi e}\, \sigma \qquad (54)$$

Here H has the meaning with which we are familiar if the unit in which σ is expressed is the "width" of one category, or alternative, along the continuum. Formula (54) may be rewritten

$$H = \log 4.133\sigma$$
$$= \log \sigma + \log 4.133$$
$$= \log \sigma + 2.04 \tag{55}$$

This equation is correct only in the case of a normal distribution, however. In the case of a *rectangular distribution*,

$$H = \log R(\text{ange}) \tag{56}$$

(This is the same as formula (1), if the "width" of a category is the unit of Range.) But for a rectangular distribution,

$$\sigma = R/\sqrt{12}$$

or

$$R = \sqrt{12}\,\sigma = 3.464\sigma$$

Therefore we may substitute in (56)

$$H = \log 3.464\sigma$$
$$= \log \sigma + \log 3.464$$
$$= \log \sigma + 1.79 \tag{57}$$

Comparing (57) with (55), we see that the uncertainty of a normal distribution is greater by .25 bits than that of a rectangular distribution with the same standard deviation. Incidentally, it may be shown that the normal distribution has greater uncertainty than any other distribution with the same σ, whereas a rectangular distribution has the greatest uncertainty possible with a given *range*.

It is evident from Figure 5 (p. 49), and from formula (20), that

$$T(x;y) = H(y) - H_x(y) \tag{58}$$

If x and y are ordered variables, correlated with each other, $H(y)$ may be considered the uncertainty of the marginal y-distribution, and $H_x(y)$ the uncertainty of the distribution of residuals about the regression line. The standard deviations of these distributions are σ_y and $\sigma_{y.x}$, respectively. If both distributions are normal, we may substitute in (58), according to (55):

$$\tilde{T}(x;y) = (\log \sigma_y + 2.04) - (\log \sigma_{y.x} + 2.04)$$

$$= \log \sigma_y - \log \sigma_{y.x}$$

$$= \log \frac{\sigma_y}{\sigma_{y.x}} \tag{59}$$

(The wave over T merely indicates that it is an estimate, of a new kind.) But it is well known (see McNemar [54] p. 109) that

$$\sigma_{y.x} = \sigma_y \sqrt{1 - r^2}$$

therefore

$$\tilde{T}(x;y) = \log \frac{1}{\sqrt{1 - r^2}} \tag{60}$$

This attractively simple formula for transforming r into T does not hold true, however, unless both y and the residuals are distributed normally. In the usual absolute judgment situation, the distribution of y will be very nearly rectangular, though the distribution of error about the regression line is typically more or less normal. When y has a rectangular distribution, the value of $H(y)$ is given by formula (57); thus we may substitute in (58):

$$\tilde{T}(x;y) = (\log \sigma_y + 1.79) - (\log \sigma_{y.x} + 2.04)$$

$$= \log \sigma_y - \log \sigma_{y.x} - .25$$

$$= \log \frac{\sigma_y}{\sigma_{y.x}} - .25 \tag{61}$$

$$= \log \frac{1}{\sqrt{1 - r^2}} - .25 \tag{62}$$

Note that in deriving formulas (60) and (62) only the *ratio* of the two σ's is important; therefore the unit in which they are expressed makes no difference. By the use of (62) one might, for example, estimate the information transmitted by a subject in reproducing the position of a point on a line, though the number of alternative stimulus positions were indefinitely great, and responses were measured as accurately as possible. Indeed, it is at the opposite extreme, when very few categories are used, that these transformations should be used most cautiously. When $r = 1.00$, the absurd value of $T = \infty$ follows from either formula (60) or (62). The formulas may not legitimately be used in this or any less obvious situation in which it is impossible, because of coarse categorizing, to obtain a reasonable estimate of "true" residual error.

It is fairly obvious that η may be substituted for r in formula (62), in the case of either a linear or a curvilinear relationship. But since the calculation of η involves the calculation of $\sigma_{y \cdot x}$ anyway, some useless steps may be saved by using formula (61). Or, more simply still, one may substitute (56) and (55) in (58), thus:

$$\tilde{T}(x;y) = \log R_y - (\log \sigma_{y \cdot x} + 2.04)$$

$$= \log \frac{R_y}{\sigma_{y \cdot x}} - 2.04 \tag{63}$$

In any such case, the estimate of T may be improved by applying Sheppard's correction for grouping to $\sigma_{y \cdot x}$, especially when there are relatively few categories along y. A nomogram indicating the effect of this correction on $H_x(y)$, and a derivation of formula (54) are given by Quastler and Blank [69].

The transformations described above provide at least a partial solution to the difficulty, discussed in the text, in which we find ourselves when $\hat{T}$ is known to have appreciable sampling bias but its degrees of freedom are indeterminate.

Appendix II

1. Table of $\log_2 n$ for $n \leqq 1000$.†
2. Table of $n \log_2 n$ for $n \leqq 500$.†
3. Graph of $p \log_2 \dfrac{1}{p}$ as a function of p.

---

† These tables were prepared at the Operational Applications Laboratory of the Air Force Cambridge Research Center.

n	$\log_2 n$	n	$\log_2 n$	n	$\log_2 n$
1	0	36	5.16992	71	6.14975
2	1.00000	37	5.20945	72	6.16992
3	1.58496	38	5.24793	73	6.18982
4	2.00000	39	5.28540	74	6.20945
5	2.32193	40	5.32193	75	6.22882
6	2.58496	41	5.35755	76	6.24793
7	2.80735	42	5.39232	77	6.26679
8	3.00000	43	5.42626	78	6.28540
9	3.16993	44	5.45943	79	6.30378
10	3.32193	45	5.49185	80	6.32193
11	3.45943	46	5.52356	81	6.33985
12	3.58496	47	5.55459	82	6.35755
13	3.70044	48	5.58496	83	6.37504
14	3.80735	49	5.61471	84	6.39232
15	3.90689	50	5.64386	85	6.40939
16	4.00000	51	5.67243	86	6.42626
17	4.08746	52	5.70044	87	6.44294
18	4.16993	53	5.72792	88	6.45943
19	4.24793	54	5.75489	89	6.47573
20	4.32193	55	5.78136	90	6.49185
21	4.39232	56	5.80736	91	6.50780
22	4.45943	57	5.83289	92	6.52356
23	4.52356	58	5.85798	93	6.53916
24	4.58496	59	5.88264	94	6.55459
25	4.64386	60	5.90689	95	6.56986
26	4.70044	61	5.93074	96	6.58496
27	4.75489	62	5.95420	97	6.59991
28	4.80736	63	5.97728	98	6.61471
29	4.85798	64	6.00000	99	6.62936
30	4.90689	65	6.02237	100	6.64386
31	4.95420	66	6.04439	101	6.65821
32	5.00000	67	6.06609	102	6.67243
33	5.04439	68	6.08746	103	6.68650
34	5.08746	69	6.10852	104	6.70044
35	5.12928	70	6.12928	105	6.71424

n	$\log_2 n$	n	$\log_2 n$	n	$\log_2 n$
106	6.72792	141	7.13955	176	7.45943
107	6.74147	142	7.14975	177	7.46761
108	6.75489	143	7.15987	178	7.47573
109	6.76818	144	7.16992	179	7.48382
110	6.78136	145	7.17991	180	7.49185
111	6.79442	146	7.18982	181	7.49985
112	6.80735	147	7.19967	182	7.50779
113	6.82018	148	7.20945	183	7.51570
114	6.83289	149	7.21917	184	7.52356
115	6.84549	150	7.22882	185	7.53138
116	6.85798	151	7.23840	186	7.53916
117	6.87036	152	7.24793	187	7.54689
118	6.88264	153	7.25739	188	7.55459
119	6.89482	154	7.26679	189	7.56224
120	6.90689	155	7.27612	190	7.56986
121	6.91886	156	7.28540	191	7.57743
122	6.93074	157	7.29462	192	7.58496
123	6.94251	158	7.30378	193	7.59246
124	6.95420	159	7.31288	194	7.59991
125	6.96578	160	7.32193	195	7.60733
126	6.97728	161	7.33092	196	7.61471
127	6.98868	162	7.33985	197	7.62205
128	7.00000	163	7.34873	198	7.62936
129	7.01123	164	7.35755	199	7.63662
130	7.02237	165	7.36632	200	7.64386
131	7.03342	166	7.37504	201	7.65105
132	7.04439	167	7.38370	202	7.65821
133	7.05528	168	7.39232	203	7.66534
134	7.06609	169	7.40088	204	7.67243
135	7.07682	170	7.40939	205	7.67948
136	7.08746	171	7.41785	206	7.68650
137	7.09803	172	7.42626	207	7.69349
138	7.10852	173	7.43463	208	7.70044
139	7.11894	174	7.44294	209	7.70736
140	7.12928	175	7.45121	210	7.71425

n	log₂n	n	log₂n	n	log₂n
211	7.72110	246	7.94251	281	8.13443
212	7.72792	247	7.94837	282	8.13955
213	7.73471	248	7.95420	283	8.14466
214	7.74147	249	7.96000	284	8.14975
215	7.74819	250	7.96578	285	8.15482
216	7.75489	251	7.97154	286	8.15987
217	7.76155	252	7.97728	287	8.16491
218	7.76818	253	7.98299	288	8.16992
219	7.77479	254	7.98868	289	8.17493
220	7.78136	255	7.99435	290	8.17991
221	7.78790	256	8.00000	291	8.18487
222	7.79442	257	8.00562	292	8.18982
223	7.80090	258	8.01123	293	8.19476
224	7.80735	259	8.01681	294	8.19967
225	7.81378	260	8.02237	295	8.20457
226	7.82018	261	8.02791	296	8.20945
227	7.82655	262	8.03342	297	8.21432
228	7.83289	263	8.03892	298	8.21917
229	7.83920	264	8.04439	299	8.22400
230	7.84549	265	8.04985	300	8.22882
231	7.85175	266	8.05528	301	8.23362
232	7.85798	267	8.06070	302	8.23840
233	7.86419	268	8.06609	303	8.24317
234	7.87036	269	8.07146	304	8.24793
235	7.87652	270	8.07682	305	8.25267
236	7.88264	271	8.08215	306	8.25739
237	7.88874	272	8.08746	307	8.26209
238	7.89482	273	8.09276	308	8.26679
239	7.90087	274	8.09803	309	8.27146
240	7.90689	275	8.10329	310	8.27612
241	7.91289	276	8.10852	311	8.28077
242	7.91886	277	8.11374	312	8.28540
243	7.92481	278	8.11894	313	8.29002
244	7.93074	279	8.12412	314	8.29462
245	7.93664	280	8.12928	315	8.29921

n	$\log_2 n$	n	$\log_2 n$	n	$\log_2 n$
316	8.30378	351	8.45533	386	8.59246
317	8.30834	352	8.45943	387	8.59619
318	8.31288	353	8.46352	388	8.59991
319	8.31741	354	8.46761	389	8.60363
320	8.32193	355	8.47168	390	8.60733
321	8.32643	356	8.47573	391	8.61103
322	8.33092	357	8.47978	392	8.61471
323	8.33539	358	8.48382	393	8.61839
324	8.33985	359	8.48784	394	8.62205
325	8.34430	360	8.49185	395	8.62571
326	8.34873	361	8.49585	396	8.62936
327	8.35315	362	8.49985	397	8.63299
328	8.35755	363	8.50383	398	8.63662
329	8.36194	364	8.50779	399	8.64024
330	8.36632	365	8.51175	400	8.64386
331	8.37069	366	8.51570	401	8.64746
332	8.37504	367	8.51964	402	8.65105
333	8.37938	368	8.52356	403	8.65464
334	8.38370	369	8.52748	404	8.65821
335	8.38802	370	8.53138	405	8.66178
336	8.39232	371	8.53528	406	8.66534
337	8.39660	372	8.53916	407	8.66888
338	8.40088	373	8.54303	408	8.67242
339	8.40514	374	8.54689	409	8.67596
340	8.40939	375	8.55075	410	8.67948
341	8.41363	376	8.55459	411	8.68299
342	8.41785	377	8.55842	412	8.68650
343	8.42206	378	8.56224	413	8.69000
344	8.42627	379	8.56605	414	8.69349
345	8.43045	380	8.56986	415	8.69697
346	8.43463	381	8.57365	416	8.70044
347	8.43879	382	8.57743	417	8.70390
348	8.44294	383	8.58120	418	8.70736
349	8.44708	384	8.58496	419	8.71081
350	8.45121	385	8.58871	420	8.71425

n	$\log_2 n$	n	$\log_2 n$	n	$\log_2 n$
421	8.71768	456	8.83289	491	8.93958
422	8.72110	457	8.83605	492	8.94251
423	8.72451	458	8.83920	493	8.94544
424	8.72792	459	8.84235	494	8.94837
425	8.73132	460	8.84549	495	8.95128
426	8.73471	461	8.84862	496	8.95420
427	8.73809	462	8.85175	497	8.95710
428	8.74147	463	8.85487	498	8.96000
429	8.74483	464	8.85798	499	8.96290
430	8.74819	465	8.86109	500	8.96578
431	8.75154	466	8.86419	501	8.96867
432	8.75489	467	8.86728	502	8.97154
433	8.75822	468	8.87036	503	8.97441
434	8.76155	469	8.87344	504	8.97728
435	8.76487	470	8.87652	505	8.98014
436	8.76818	471	8.87958	506	8.98299
437	8.77149	472	8.88264	507	8.98584
438	8.77479	473	8.88570	508	8.98868
439	8.77808	474	8.88874	509	8.99152
440	8.78136	475	8.89178	510	8.99435
441	8.78463	476	8.89482	511	8.99718
442	8.78790	477	8.89784	512	9.00000
443	8.79116	478	8.90087	513	9.00281
444	8.79442	479	8.90388	514	9.00562
445	8.79766	480	8.90689	515	9.00843
446	8.80090	481	8.90989	516	9.01123
447	8.80413	482	8.91289	517	9.01402
448	8.80735	483	8.91588	518	9.01681
449	8.81057	484	8.91886	519	9.01959
450	8.81378	485	8.92184	520	9.02237
451	8.81698	486	8.92481	521	9.02514
452	8.82018	487	8.92778	522	9.02791
453	8.82337	488	8.93074	523	9.03067
454	8.82655	489	8.93369	524	9.03342
455	8.82972	490	8.93664	525	9.03617

n	$\log_2 n$	n	$\log_2 n$	n	$\log_2 n$
526	9.03892	561	9.13186	596	9.21917
527	9.04166	562	9.13443	597	9.22159
528	9.04439	563	9.13699	598	9.22400
529	9.04712	564	9.13955	599	9.22641
530	9.04985	565	9.14211	600	9.22882
531	9.05257	566	9.14466	601	9.23122
532	9.05528	567	9.14720	602	9.23362
533	9.05799	568	9.14975	603	9.23601
534	9.06070	569	9.15228	604	9.23840
535	9.06340	570	9.15482	605	9.24079
536	9.06609	571	9.15735	606	9.24317
537	9.06878	572	9.15987	607	9.24555
538	9.07146	573	9.16239	608	9.24793
539	9.07414	574	9.16491	609	9.25030
540	9.07682	575	9.16742	610	9.25267
541	9.07948	576	9.16993	611	9.25503
542	9.08215	577	9.17243	612	9.25739
543	9.08481	578	9.17493	613	9.25974
544	9.08746	579	9.17742	614	9.26209
545	9.09011	580	9.17991	615	9.26444
546	9.09276	581	9.18239	616	9.26679
547	9.09540	582	9.18487	617	9.26913
548	9.09803	583	9.18735	618	9.27146
549	9.10066	584	9.18982	619	9.27379
550	9.10329	585	9.19229	620	9.27612
551	9.10591	586	9.19476	621	9.27845
552	9.10852	587	9.19722	622	9.28077
553	9.11114	588	9.19967	623	9.28309
554	9.11374	589	9.20212	624	9.28540
555	9.11634	590	9.20457	625	9.28771
556	9.11894	591	9.20701	626	9.29002
557	9.12153	592	9.20945	627	9.29232
558	9.12412	593	9.21189	628	9.29462
559	9.12670	594	9.21432	629	9.29691
560	9.12928	595	9.21675	630	9.29921

n	$\log_2 n$	n	$\log_2 n$	n	$\log_2 n$
631	9.30150	666	9.37938	701	9.45327
632	9.30378	667	9.38154	702	9.45533
633	9.30606	668	9.38370	703	9.45738
634	9.30834	669	9.38586	704	9.45943
635	9.31061	670	9.38802	705	9.46148
636	9.31288	671	9.39017	706	9.46352
637	9.31515	672	9.39232	707	9.46557
638	9.31741	673	9.39446	708	9.46761
639	9.31967	674	9.39660	709	9.46964
640	9.32193	675	9.39874	710	9.47167
641	9.32418	676	9.40088	711	9.47370
642	9.32643	677	9.40301	712	9.47573
643	9.32868	678	9.40514	713	9.47776
644	9.33092	679	9.40727	714	9.47978
645	9.33315	680	9.40939	715	9.48180
646	9.33539	681	9.41151	716	9.48382
647	9.33762	682	9.41363	717	9.48583
648	9.33985	683	9.41574	718	9.48784
649	9.34207	684	9.41785	719	9.48985
650	9.34430	685	9.41996	720	9.49185
651	9.34651	686	9.42207	721	9.49385
652	9.34873	687	9.42417	722	9.49585
653	9.35094	688	9.42626	723	9.49785
654	9.35315	689	9.42836	724	9.49985
655	9.35535	690	9.43045	725	9.50184
656	9.35755	691	9.43254	726	9.50383
657	9.35975	692	9.43463	727	9.50581
658	9.36194	693	9.43671	728	9.50779
659	9.36414	694	9.43879	729	9.50978
660	9.36632	695	9.44087	730	9.51175
661	9.36851	696	9.44294	731	9.51373
662	9.37069	697	9.44501	732	9.51570
663	9.37286	698	9.44708	733	9.51767
664	9.37504	699	9.44915	734	9.51964
665	9.37721	700	9.45121	735	9.52160

n	$\log_2 n$	n	$\log_2 n$	n	$\log_2 n$
736	9.52356	771	9.59059	806	9.65464
737	9.52552	772	9.59246	807	9.65643
738	9.52748	773	9.59432	808	9.65821
739	9.52943	774	9.59619	809	9.66000
740	9.53138	775	9.59805	810	9.66178
741	9.53333	776	9.59991	811	9.66356
742	9.53527	777	9.60177	812	9.66534
743	9.53722	778	9.60363	813	9.66711
744	9.53916	779	9.60548	814	9.66888
745	9.54110	780	9.60733	815	9.67066
746	9.54303	781	9.60918	816	9.67242
747	9.54496	782	9.61102	817	9.67419
748	9.54689	783	9.61287	818	9.67596
749	9.54882	784	9.61471	819	9.67772
750	9.55075	785	9.61655	820	9.67948
751	9.55267	786	9.61839	821	9.68124
752	9.55459	787	9.62022	822	9.68299
753	9.55651	788	9.62205	823	9.68475
754	9.55842	789	9.62388	824	9.68650
755	9.56033	790	9.62571	825	9.68825
756	9.56224	791	9.62753	826	9.69000
757	9.56415	792	9.62936	827	9.69174
758	9.56605	793	9.63118	828	9.69349
759	9.56796	794	9.63299	829	9.69523
760	9.56985	795	9.63481	830	9.69697
761	9.57175	796	9.63662	831	9.69870
762	9.57365	797	9.63844	832	9.70044
763	9.57554	798	9.64025	833	9.70217
764	9.57743	799	9.64205	834	9.70390
765	9.57932	800	9.64386	835	9.70563
766	9.58120	801	9.64566	836	9.70736
767	9.58308	802	9.64746	837	9.70908
768	9.58496	803	9.64926	838	9.71081
769	9.58684	804	9.65105	839	9.71253
770	9.58872	805	9.65284	840	9.71425

n	$\log_2 n$	n	$\log_2 n$	n	$\log_2 n$
841	9.71596	876	9.77479	911	9.83131
842	9.71768	877	9.77643	912	9.83289
843	9.71939	878	9.77808	913	9.83447
844	9.72110	879	9.77972	914	9.83605
845	9.72281	880	9.78136	915	9.83763
846	9.72451	881	9.78300	916	9.83920
847	9.72622	882	9.78463	917	9.84078
848	9.72792	883	9.78627	918	9.84235
849	9.72962	884	9.78790	919	9.84392
850	9.73132	885	9.78953	920	9.84549
851	9.73301	886	9.79116	921	9.84706
852	9.73471	887	9.79279	922	9.84862
853	9.73640	888	9.79442	923	9.85019
854	9.73809	889	9.79604	924	9.85175
855	9.73978	890	9.79766	925	9.85331
856	9.74147	891	9.79928	926	9.85487
857	9.74315	892	9.80090	927	9.85643
858	9.74483	893	9.80252	928	9.85798
859	9.74651	894	9.80413	929	9.85953
860	9.74819	895	9.80574	930	9.86109
861	9.74987	896	9.80735	931	9.86264
862	9.75154	897	9.80896	932	9.86419
863	9.75322	898	9.81057	933	9.86573
864	9.75489	899	9.81218	934	9.86728
865	9.75656	900	9.81378	935	9.86882
866	9.75822	901	9.81538	936	9.87036
867	9.75989	902	9.81698	937	9.87190
868	9.76155	903	9.81858	938	9.87344
869	9.76321	904	9.82018	939	9.87498
870	9.76487	905	9.82177	940	9.87652
871	9.76653	906	9.82337	941	9.87805
872	9.76818	907	9.82496	942	9.87958
873	9.76984	908	9.82655	943	9.88111
874	9.77149	909	9.82814	944	9.88264
875	9.77314	910	9.82972	945	9.88417

n	$\log_2 n$	n	$\log_2 n$	n	$\log_2 n$
946	9.88570	981	9.93811		
947	9.88722	982	9.93958		
948	9.88874	983	9.94105		
949	9.89026	984	9.94251		
950	9.89178	985	9.94398		
951	9.89330	986	9.94544		
952	9.89482	987	9.94691		
953	9.89633	988	9.94837		
954	9.89785	989	9.94983		
955	9.89936	990	9.95128		
956	9.90087	991	9.95274		
957	9.90237	992	9.95420		
958	9.90388	993	9.95565		
959	9.90539	994	9.95710		
960	9.90689	995	9.95855		
961	9.90839	996	9.96000		
962	9.90989	997	9.96145		
963	9.91139	998	9.96290		
964	9.91289	999	9.96434		
965	9.91438	1000	9.96578		
966	9.91588				
967	9.91737				
968	9.91886				
969	9.92035				
970	9.92184				
971	9.92333				
972	9.92481				
973	9.92630				
974	9.92778				
975	9.92926				
976	9.93074				
977	9.93221				
978	9.93369				
979	9.93517				
980	9.93664				

n	$n \log_2 n$	n	$n \log_2 n$	n	$n \log_2 n$
0	0				
1	0	36	186.11730	71	436.63205
2	2.00000	37	192.74977	72	444.23460
3	4.75489	38	199.42125	73	451.85719
4	8.00000	39	206.13069	74	459.49955
5	11.60964	40	212.87712	75	467.16140
6	15.50977	41	219.65963	76	474.84249
7	19.65148	42	226.47733	77	482.54256
8	24.00000	43	233.32938	78	490.26137
9	28.52932	44	240.21499	79	497.99868
10	33.21928	45	247.13339	80	505.75425
11	38.05375	46	254.08385	81	513.52785
12	43.01955	47	261.06568	82	521.31926
13	48.10572	48	268.07820	83	529.12827
14	53.30297	49	275.12078	84	536.95466
15	58.60336	50	282.19281	85	544.79823
16	64.00000	51	289.29369	86	552.65877
17	69.48687	52	296.42287	87	560.53608
18	75.05865	53	303.57978	88	568.42998
19	80.71062	54	310.76393	89	576.34028
20	86.43856	55	317.97478	90	584.26678
21	92.23867	56	325.21188	91	592.20931
22	98.10750	57	332.47473	92	600.16770
23	104.04192	58	339.76290	93	608.14177
24	110.03910	59	347.07594	94	616.13135
25	116.09640	60	354.41344	95	624.13628
26	122.21143	61	361.77498	96	632.15640
27	128.38196	62	369.16017	97	640.19155
28	134.60594	63	376.56864	98	648.24156
29	140.88145	64	384.00000	99	656.30631
30	147.20672	65	391.45391	100	664.38562
31	153.58009	66	398.93001	101	672.47936
32	160.00000	67	406.42798	102	680.58738
33	166.46501	68	413.94747	103	688.70955
34	172.97374	69	421.48819	104	696.84573
35	179.52491	70	429.04981	105	704.99578

n	n log₂ n	n	n log₂ n	n	n log₂ n

n	$n \log_2 n$	n	$n \log_2 n$	n	$n \log_2 n$
106	713.15957	141	1006.67674	176	1312.85996
107	721.33697	142	1015.26409	177	1321.76618
108	729.52785	143	1023.86160	178	1330.68055
109	737.73209	144	1032.46920	179	1339.60302
110	745.94957	145	1041.08682	180	1348.53356
111	754.18016	146	1049.71439	181	1357.47210
112	762.42375	147	1058.35183	182	1366.41862
113	770.68022	148	1066.99910	183	1375.37307
114	778.94946	149	1075.65611	184	1384.33540
115	787.23136	150	1084.32280	185	1393.30557
116	795.52579	151	1092.99911	186	1402.28354
117	803.83267	152	1101.68498	187	1411.26926
118	812.15188	153	1110.38034	188	1420.26270
119	820.48331	154	1119.08513	189	1429.26382
120	828.82687	155	1127.79928	190	1438.27256
121	837.18245	156	1136.52275	191	1447.28891
122	845.54995	157	1145.25546	192	1456.31280
123	853.92928	158	1153.99736	193	1465.34421
124	862.32034	159	1162.74839	194	1474.38309
125	870.72304	160	1171.50849	195	1483.42941
126	879.13727	161	1180.27762	196	1492.48313
127	887.56295	162	1189.05570	197	1501.54421
128	896.00000	163	1197.84269	198	1510.61261
129	904.44832	164	1206.63853	199	1519.68830
130	912.90782	165	1215.44316	200	1528.77124
131	921.37841	166	1224.25654	201	1537.86139
132	929.86002	167	1233.07862	202	1546.95872
133	938.35256	168	1241.90933	203	1556.06319
134	946.85595	169	1250.74862	204	1565.17477
135	955.37010	170	1259.59646	205	1574.29342
136	963.89495	171	1268.45278	206	1583.41911
137	972.43039	172	1277.31754	207	1592.55180
138	980.97637	173	1286.19068	208	1601.69146
139	989.53281	174	1295.07217	209	1610.83806
140	998.09962	175	1303.96194	210	1619.99156

n	n log₂ n	n	n log₂ n	n	n log₂ n
211	1629.15193	246	1953.85857	281	2285.77380
212	1638.31914	247	1963.24671	282	2295.35348
213	1647.49315	248	1972.64069	283	2304.93828
214	1656.67394	249	1982.04048	284	2314.52818
215	1665.86146	250	1991.44607	285	2324.12316
216	1675.05570	251	2000.85743	286	2333.72320
217	1684.25662	252	2010.27454	287	2343.32829
218	1693.46418	253	2019.69737	288	2352.93840
219	1702.67837	254	2029.12591	289	2362.55352
220	1711.89914	255	2038.56013	290	2372.17364
221	1721.12647	256	2048.00000	291	2381.79872
222	1730.36032	257	2057.44551	292	2391.42877
223	1739.60068	258	2066.89663	293	2401.06376
224	1748.84750	259	2076.35335	294	2410.70367
225	1758.10077	260	2085.81563	295	2420.34849
226	1767.36045	261	2095.28347	296	2429.99820
227	1776.62651	262	2104.75683	297	2439.65278
228	1785.89892	263	2114.23569	298	2449.31222
229	1795.17767	264	2123.72005	299	2458.97650
230	1804.46271	265	2133.20987	300	2468.64561
231	1813.75403	266	2142.70513	301	2478.31952
232	1823.05159	267	2152.20581	302	2487.99823
233	1832.35537	268	2161.71190	303	2497.68172
234	1841.66534	269	2171.22338	304	2507.36996
235	1850.98148	270	2180.74021	305	2517.06296
236	1860.30376	271	2190.26239	306	2526.76068
237	1869.63215	272	2199.78989	307	2536.46312
238	1878.96663	273	2209.32270	308	2546.17025
239	1888.30717	274	2218.86079	309	2555.88208
240	1897.65374	275	2228.40415	310	2565.59857
241	1907.00633	276	2237.95275	311	2575.31971
242	1916.36490	277	2247.50658	312	2585.04549
243	1925.72944	278	2257.06562	313	2594.77590
244	1935.09991	279	2266.62985	314	2604.51092
245	1944.47630	280	2276.19924	315	2614.25053

n	n log₂ n	n	n log₂ n	n	n log₂ n
316	2623.99472	351	2967.81985	386	3316.68842
317	2633.74347	352	2977.71993	387	3326.72544
318	2643.49678	353	2987.62410	388	3336.76618
319	2653.25462	354	2997.53237	389	3346.81065
320	2663.01699	355	3007.44470	390	3356.85882
321	2672.78387	356	3017.36110	391	3366.91070
322	2682.55524	357	3027.28155	392	3376.96626
323	2692.33108	358	303 7.20605	393	3387.02550
324	2702.11140	359	3047.13457	394	3397.08842
325	2711.89617	360	3057.06711	395	3407.15499
326	2721.68538	361	3067.00366	396	3417.22522
327	2731.47901	362	3076.94421	397	3427.29909
328	2741.27706	363	3086.88874	398	3437.37660
329	2751.07950	364	3096.83725	399	3447.45773
330	2760.88633	365	3106.78972	400	3457.54248
331	2770.69753	366	3116.74614	401	3467.63083
332	2780.51309	367	3126.70650	402	3477.72278
333	2790.33300	368	3136.67080	403	3487.81832
334	2800.15723	369	3146.63902	404	3497.91744
335	2809.98579	370	3156.61114	405	3508.02013
336	2819.81865	371	3166.58717	406	3518.12638
337	2829.65581	372	3176.56708	407	3528.23619
338	2839.49725	373	3186.55087	408	3538.34954
339	2849.34296	374	3196.53853	409	3548.46643
340	2859.19292	375	3206.53004	410	3558.58684
341	2869.04712	376	3216.52541	411	3568.71077
342	2878.90556	377	3226.52461	412	3578.83822
343	2888.76822	378	3236.52764	413	3588.96916
344	2898.63508	379	3246.53448	414	3599.10360
345	2908.50613	380	3256.54513	415	3609.24152
346	2918.38137	381	3266.55958	416	3619.38292
347	2928.26077	382	3276.57781	417	3629.52779
348	2938.14434	383	3286.59982	418	3639.67612
349	2948.03205	384	3296.62560	419	3649.82790
350	2957.92389	385	3306.65513	420	3659.98312

n	n log₂ n	n	n log₂ n	n	n log₂ n
421	3670.14177	456	4027.79785	491	4389.33339
422	3680.30386	457	4038.07501	492	4399.71714
423	3690.46936	458	4048.35534	493	4410.10381
424	3700.63827	459	4058.63881	494	4420.49341
425	3710.81059	460	4068.92542	495	4430.88593
426	3720.98630	461	4079.21518	496	4441.28137
427	3731.16540	462	4089.50806	497	4451.67971
428	3741.34787	463	4099.80406	498	4462.08096
429	3751.53372	464	4110.10318	499	4472.48511
430	3761.72293	465	4120.40541	500	4482.89214
431	3771.91549	466	4130.71074		
432	3782.11140	467	4141.01917		
433	3792.31065	468	4151.33069		
434	3802.51324	469	4161.64529		
435	3812.71914	470	4171.96297		
436	3822.92837	471	4182.28371		
437	3833.14090	472	4192.60752		
438	3843.35673	473	4202.93438		
439	3853.57586	474	4213.26430		
440	3863.79827	475	4223.59726		
441	3874.02397	476	4233.93326		
442	3884.25293	477	4244.27228		
443	3894.48516	478	4254.61433		
444	3904.72064	479	4264.95940		
445	3914.95938	480	4275.30749		
446	3925.20136	481	4285.65857		
447	3935.44657	482	4296.01266		
448	3945.69501	483	4306.36974		
449	3955.94666	484	4316.72981		
450	3966.20154	485	4327.09285		
451	3976.45961	486	4337.45888		
452	3986.72089	487	4347.82787		
453	3996.98536	488	4358.19982		
454	4007.25301	489	4368.57473		
455	4017.52384	490	4378.95259		

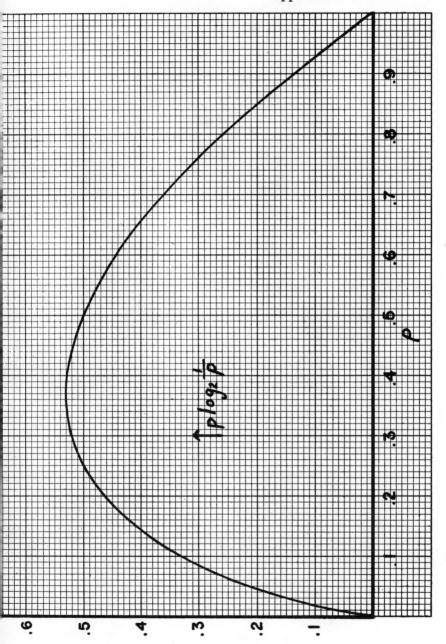